UIC The University of Illinois at Chicago

The original edition was based on work supported by the National Science Foundation under grant No. MDR 9050226 and the University of Illinois at Chicago. Any opinions, findings, and conclusions or recommendations expressed in this publication are those of the author(s) and do not necessarily reflect the views of the granting agencies.

LETTER HOME
Using Fractions

Date: _____

Dear Family Member:

In this unit, your child will use pattern blocks to explore fractions. For example, the figure on the right shows how a student might use pattern blocks to solve the following problem: *Carl ordered a pizza. One-half of the pizza had sausage on it. One-half of that half also had mushrooms. What fraction of the pizza had sausage and mushrooms?* The number sentence $\frac{1}{2} \times \frac{1}{2} = \frac{1}{4}$ represents this problem.

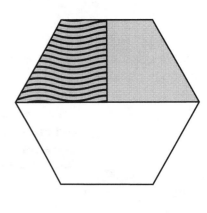

$\frac{1}{2}$ of $\frac{1}{2}$ is $\frac{1}{4}$

Using pattern block pieces in their investigation of fractions and engaging in other activities such as paper folding, students explore patterns that will help them develop paper-and-pencil methods for multiplying fractions.

During this unit, your child will also explore mixed numbers. Students will find different ways to name mixed numbers. For example, $\frac{13}{4}$ can also be named as $3\frac{1}{4}$ or 2 and $\frac{5}{4}$. They will apply this skill as they add mixed numbers.

As we work through this unit:

- Encourage your child to draw pictures and explain to you the strategies he or she uses to solve homework problems involving fractions.

- Ask your child to share the Adventure Book *Peanut Soup.*

- Help your child review for the midterm test by having him or her share the *Party Problems* with you.

Sincerely,

_____

UNIT OUTLINE

Using Fractions

Pacing Suggestions

This unit is designed to be completed in 7 to 9 days as shown on the Unit Outline below.

- Lesson 6 *Peanut Soup* is an Adventure Book story taken from a true incident in the life of George Washington Carver. Students can read this story during language arts or social studies time.
- Lesson 7 *Party Problems* is an optional lesson in which students solve multistep word problems. These problems can be assigned for homework to prepare students for the midterm test in Lesson 8. They are also appropriate to use in class with a substitute teacher since preparation is minimal.

Components Key: SG = Student Guide, DAB = Discovery Assignment Book, AB = Adventure Book, URG = Unit Resource Guide, and DPP = Daily Practice and Problems

	Sessions	Description	Supplies
LESSON 1 **Hexagon Duets** SG pages 376–379 DAB page 193 URG pages 16–23 DPP A–B	1–2	**ACTIVITY:** Addition of mixed numbers is introduced through the use of a game. Students find equivalent representations of mixed numbers.	• pattern blocks • spinners
LESSON 2 **Adding Mixed Numbers** SG pages 380–382 URG pages 24–30 DPP C–D	1	**ACTIVITY:** Students model addition of mixed numbers using pattern blocks; then they develop paper-and-pencil methods.	• pattern blocks
LESSON 3 **Fractions of Groups** SG pages 383–386 URG pages 31–38 DPP E–F	1	**ACTIVITY:** Using diagrams, students develop procedures for multiplying a fraction times a whole number.	

	Sessions	Description	Supplies
LESSON 4 **Multiplication of Fractions** SG pages 387–389 DAB pages 195–197 URG pages 39–48 DPP G–H	1	**ACTIVITY:** Using pattern blocks, students multiply fractions times whole numbers and fractions times fractions.	• pattern blocks
LESSON 5 **Using Patterns to Multiply Fractions** SG pages 390–391 URG pages 49–56 DPP I–J	1	**ACTIVITY:** Students fold paper to model multiplication of fractions. The patterns they see help them develop procedures for multiplying fractions with paper and pencil.	• scrap paper • crayons or colored pencils
LESSON 6 **Peanut Soup** AB pages 77–92 URG pages 57–65 DPP K–L	1	**ADVENTURE BOOK:** This story tells how George Washington Carver was able to convince businessmen of the economic value of peanuts by inviting them to a meal made from peanut products. As they prepare the meal, Carver's students use fractions to convert recipes to the needed size.	
LESSON 7 **Party Problems** SG pages 392–393 URG pages 66–68	– OPTIONAL LESSON –		
	1	**OPTIONAL ACTIVITY:** Students solve word problems in the context of a birthday party.	• calculators
LESSON 8 **Midterm Test** URG pages 69–79 DPP M–N	1	**ASSESSMENT ACTIVITY:** Students complete a test involving concepts covered in this and previous units. **ASSESSMENT PAGES:** *Midterm Test,* Unit Resource Guide, pages 72–77.	• pattern blocks • rulers • calculators

A current list of connections is available at www.kendallhunt.com.

Software   **Suggested Titles**

- *Compare with Ratios* introduces students to recognizing and using ratios.
- *Fraction Attraction* develops understanding of fractions using fraction bars, pie charts, hundreds blocks, and other materials.
- *Fraction Operation* develops conceptual understanding of fraction operations, including finding common denominators.
- *Math Arena* is a collection of math activities that reinforces many math concepts.
- *Math Munchers Deluxe* provides practice with basic facts and finding equivalent fractions, decimals, percents, ratios, angles and identifying geometric shapes, factors, and multiples in an arcade-like game.
- *Math Mysteries Advanced Fractions* develops multistep problem solving with fractions.
- *Mighty Math Number Heroes* poses short answer questions about different math topics including fractions.
- *National Library of Virtual Manipulatives* website (http://matti.usu.edu) allows students to work with manipulatives including pattern blocks.

PREPARING FOR UPCOMING LESSONS

Begin collecting lids and cans of different sizes for the lab *Circumference vs. Diameter* in Unit 14.

BACKGROUND

Using Fractions

In this unit, students continue their study of fractions. The activities build upon and extend previous activities in Units 3, 5, 9, and 11 of fifth grade. All of the fraction work in the curriculum is built on a solid conceptual foundation so that students can develop and apply procedures and skills. Among the concepts and skills students must acquire is the ability to represent and identify fractions in equivalent forms. The Number and Operations Standard of the *Principles and Standards for School Mathematics* states:

> "Representing numbers with various physical materials should be a major part of mathematics instruction in the elementary school grades. By the middle grades, students should understand that numbers can be represented in various ways, so that they see that $\frac{1}{4}$, 25%, and 0.25 are all different names for the same number. Students' understanding and ability to reason will grow as they represent fractions and decimals with physical materials and on number lines and as they learn to generate equivalent representations of fractions and decimals." (NCTM, 2000)

The activities in this unit use pattern blocks to represent various equivalent forms of the same number. Students have many opportunities to move between concrete models and symbolic representations of a number. This ability to read, use, and appreciate multiple representations of the same quantity is a critical step in learning to understand and do mathematics. For example, to add mixed numbers it is important for students to understand that $2\frac{3}{4}$, $2\frac{6}{8}$, and $1\frac{14}{8}$ all represent the same quantity.

Modeling the same fraction in different ways helps students generalize concepts and procedures and apply them to new situations. Using diagrams of collections of objects, paper folding, and pattern blocks, students model multiplication of fractions and look for patterns that will help them find efficient methods for multiplying a whole number times a fraction and a fraction times a fraction. See Figure 1.

As students learn to add mixed numbers and multiply fractions, the focus of instruction is on building conceptual understanding in contrast to teaching rote procedures. This understanding provides a foundation for later work with rational expressions in algebra.

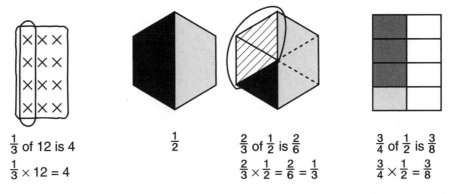

$\frac{1}{3}$ of 12 is 4
$\frac{1}{3} \times 12 = 4$

$\frac{1}{2}$

$\frac{2}{3}$ of $\frac{1}{2}$ is $\frac{2}{6}$
$\frac{2}{3} \times \frac{1}{2} = \frac{2}{6} = \frac{1}{3}$

$\frac{3}{4}$ of $\frac{1}{2}$ is $\frac{3}{8}$
$\frac{3}{4} \times \frac{1}{2} = \frac{3}{8}$

Figure 1: *Three models for multiplying fractions*

Resources

- Behr, M.J., and T.R. Post. "Teaching Rational Number and Decimal Concepts." In *Teaching Mathematics in Grades K–8: Research Based Methods.* Allyn and Bacon, Boston, 1992.
- Burns, Marilyn. *About Teaching Mathematics. A K–8 Resource.* Math Solutions Publications, White Plains, NY, 1992.
- Cramer, K., M. Behr, and T. Post. *Rational Number Project: Lessons for the Middle Grades—Levels 1 and 2.* Kendall/Hunt, Dubuque, IA, 1998.
- Cramer, K., T. Post, and R. del Mas. "Initial Fraction Learning by Fourth- and Fifth-Grade Students: A Comparison of the Effects of Using Commercial Curricula with the Effects of Using the Rational Number Project Curriculum." *Journal for Research in Mathematics Education,* 33(2), pp. 111–144, March 2002.
- Phillips, Elizabeth, et al. *Understanding Rational Numbers and Proportions* from the Curriculum and Evaluation Standards Addenda Series, Grades 5–8. The National Council of Teachers of Mathematics, Reston, VA, 1992.
- *Principles and Standards for School Mathematics.* The National Council of Teachers of Mathematics, Reston, VA, 2000.

Assessment Indicators

- Can students add and subtract fractions using pattern blocks and paper and pencil?
- Can students reduce fractions to lowest terms?
- Can students rename mixed numbers?
- Can students estimate sums of mixed numbers?
- Can students add mixed numbers using pattern blocks and paper and pencil?
- Can students estimate products of fractions?
- Can students multiply a fraction and a whole number?
- Can students multiply fractions using pattern blocks, paper folding, and paper and pencil?
- Do students solve problems in more than one way?

OBSERVATIONAL ASSESSMENT RECORD

(A1) Can students add and subtract fractions using pattern blocks and paper and pencil?

(A2) Can students reduce fractions to lowest terms?

(A3) Can students rename mixed numbers?

(A4) Can students estimate sums of mixed numbers?

(A5) Can students add mixed numbers using pattern blocks and paper and pencil?

(A6) Can students estimate products of fractions?

(A7) Can students multiply a fraction and a whole number?

(A8) Can students multiply fractions using pattern blocks, paper folding, and paper and pencil?

(A9) Do students solve problems in more than one way?

(A10) _____

Name	A1	A2	A3	A4	A5	A6	A7	A8	A9	A10	Comments
1.											
2.											
3.											
4.											
5.											
6.											
7.											
8.											
9.											
10.											
11.											
12.											
13.											

Name	A1	A2	A3	A4	A5	A6	A7	A8	A9	A10	Comments
14.											
15.											
16.											
17.											
18.											
19.											
20.											
21.											
22.											
23.											
24.											
25.											
26.											
27.											
28.											
29.											
30.											
31.											
32.											

Daily Practice and Problems

Using Fractions

A DPP Menu for Unit 12

Eight icons designate the subject matter of the DPP items. Each DPP item may fall into one or more of the categories listed below. The icons appear in the Teacher Notes column in each of the DPP items. Below is a brief menu of the DPP items included in Unit 12.

N Number Sense	**Computation**	**Time**	**Geometry**
B, C, F, H–J L–N	B–D, F, H–N		C, D
Math Facts	**$ Money**	**Measurement**	**Data**
A, E, G, I, K, M	N	B, D	

Two DPP items are included for each class session listed in the Unit Outline. The first item is always a Bit and the second is either a Task or a Challenge. The *Daily Practice and Problems and Home Practice Guide* in the *Teacher Implementation Guide* includes information on how and when to use the DPP. A *Scope and Sequence Chart* for the Daily Practice and Problems for the year can also be found in the *Teacher Implementation Guide*.

Review of Math Facts

By the end of fourth grade, students in *Math Trailblazers™* are expected to demonstrate fluency with all the division facts. The DPP for this unit continues the systematic approach to reviewing the division facts. This unit reviews the related division facts in the group of multiplication facts known as the last six facts. Since there are two related division facts for each multiplication fact, there are 12 division facts in this group ($24 \div 6 = 4$, $24 \div 4 = 6$, $28 \div 4 = 7$, $28 \div 7 = 4$, $32 \div 8 = 4$, $32 \div 4 = 8$, $42 \div 6 = 7$, $42 \div 7 = 6$, $48 \div 6 = 8$, $48 \div 8 = 6$, $56 \div 8 = 7$, $56 \div 7 = 8$).

For more information about the distribution and assessment of the math facts, see the TIMS Tutor: *Math Facts* in the *Teacher Implementation Guide* and the *Grade 5 Facts Resource Guide*.

Daily Practice and Problems

Students may solve the items individually, in groups, or as a class. The items may also be assigned for homework.

Student Questions	Teacher Notes

 Practice: Last Six Facts

A. 48 ÷ 6 =   B. 56 ÷ 8 =

C. 24 ÷ 4 =   D. 32 ÷ 8 =

E. 42 ÷ 6 =   F. 28 ÷ 7 =

TIMS Bit

A. 8   B. 7

C. 6   D. 4

E. 7   F. 4

B **Making a Map**

Frank made a map of his classroom. 1 cm on his map represents 50 centimeters in the classroom. He drew a straight line on his map from the teacher's desk to the garbage can. Then, he drew a straight line from the garbage can to the door. He made these measurements:

- The distance from the teacher's desk to the garbage can is 2.4 cm.

- The distance from the garbage can to the door is 4.6 cm.

Use Frank's measurements to predict the actual distance in the classroom from Mr. Moreno's desk to the garbage can, and then to the door.

TIMS Challenge

The predicted total distance is 350 cm or 3.5 m.

Student Questions	Teacher Notes

Do You See a Triangle?

In each case, tell whether the given lengths will make a triangle. Justify your answer. (*Hint:* Estimation is an appropriate strategy for solving this problem.)

A. 3 inches, 4 inches, 6 inches

B. $3\frac{1}{2}$ inches, 8 inches, $4\frac{5}{8}$ inches

C. $15\frac{3}{16}$ inches, $7\frac{1}{4}$ inches, $7\frac{3}{8}$ inches

TIMS Bit

Encourage students to estimate for B and C.

A. Yes, because 3 inches + 4 inches > 6 inches

B. Yes, $3\frac{1}{2}$ inches + $4\frac{5}{8}$ inches > 8 inches

C. No, $7\frac{1}{4}$ inches + $7\frac{3}{8}$ inches < 15 inches

Making a Quilt

1. Mrs. Sorenson is teaching the students in Mr. Moreno's class how to make a patchwork quilt. The entire quilt will be a rectangle measuring 4 feet by 5 feet. The quilt will be made up of individual squares, each measuring 6 inches by 6 inches. How many individual squares are needed to make the quilt? Explain how you solved the problem.

2. There are 22 students in Mr. Moreno's class. The students are going to cut the individual squares from scraps of material. How many individual squares should each student cut out in order to have enough squares for the quilt?

TIMS Challenge

Encourage students to draw a picture to help them solve the problem. Strategies will vary. One possible solution:

1. 4 feet = 48 inches; 5 feet = 60 inches; Eight individual squares can fit along the length of 48 inches. Ten individual squares can fit along the width of 60 inches. 8 × 10 = 80 squares

2. 8 students must cut out 3 squares. 14 students must cut out 4 squares.

Student Questions	Teacher Notes

E Division Facts

A. $240 \div 40 =$

B. $4800 \div 60 =$

C. $2800 \div 700 =$

D. $560 \div 70 =$

E. $42,000 \div 600 =$

F. $3200 \div 80 =$

TIMS Bit

A. 6

B. 80

C. 4

D. 8

E. 70

F. 40

F Practicing the Operations

Use paper and pencil to solve the following problems. Estimate to be sure your answers are reasonable. For A and B, write your answer (the quotient) as a mixed number. Fractions should be in lowest terms.

1. A. $636 \div 16 =$

   B. $1994 \div 8 =$

   C. $467 \times 8 =$

   D. $37.2 + 125.06 =$

   E. $1045.35 - 76.3 =$

   F. $0.7 \times 85 =$

2. Explain your estimation strategy for 1F.

TIMS Task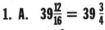

1. A. $39\frac{12}{16} = 39\frac{3}{4}$

   B. $249\frac{2}{8} = 249\frac{1}{4}$

   C. 3736

   D. 162.26

   E. 969.05

   F. 59.5

2. Seven-tenths (.7) is close to 0.75 or $\frac{3}{4}$. $\frac{3}{4}$ of 80 is 60.

Division Facts

Find the number n that makes each sentence true.

- A. $42 \div 7 = n$
- B. $320 \div 4 = n$
- C. $56 \div n = 7$
- D. $28 \div n = 7$
- E. $n \div 6 = 4$
- F. $n \div 8 = 6$

TIMS Bit

- A. 6
- B. 80
- C. 8
- D. 4
- E. 24
- F. 48

Adding Mixed Numbers

Use paper and pencil to solve the following problems. Write all fractions in lowest terms. Estimate to see if your answers are reasonable.

- A. $8\frac{7}{10} + 2\frac{1}{10} =$
- B. $2\frac{5}{9} + 3\frac{1}{3} =$
- C. $3\frac{1}{12} + 4\frac{3}{8} =$
- D. $5\frac{5}{6} + 2\frac{1}{2} =$
- E. $5\frac{7}{10} + 2\frac{3}{5} =$

TIMS Task

- A. $10\frac{8}{10} = 10\frac{4}{5}$
- B. $5\frac{8}{9}$
- C. $7\frac{11}{24}$
- D. $8\frac{1}{3}$
- E. $8\frac{3}{10}$

More Division Fact Practice

Find the number n that makes each sentence true.

- A. $56 \div n = 8$
- B. $480 \div n = 60$
- C. $n \times 400 = 24{,}000$
- D. $80 \times n = 3200$
- E. $60 \times n = 420$
- F. $n \div 7 = 400$

TIMS Bit

- A. 7
- B. 8
- C. 60
- D. 40
- E. 7
- F. 2800

Granola Bars

Lin's favorite granola bars come in packages of 10.

How many bars are in:

A. $\frac{1}{2}$ of a package?

B. $\frac{1}{10}$ of a package?

C. $\frac{3}{10}$ of a package?

D. $\frac{1}{5}$ of a package?

E. $\frac{3}{5}$ of a package?

F. $1\frac{1}{2}$ packages?

TIMS Task

A. 5

B. 1

C. 3

D. 2

E. 6

F. 15

K **Division**

Try to solve the following problems in your head. Write the quotients as mixed numbers. Fractions should be in lowest terms.

A. $30 \div 7 =$ 　　B. $60 \div 8 =$

C. $47 \div 6 =$ 　　D. $26 \div 6 =$

E. $51 \div 6 =$ 　　F. $35 \div 4 =$

TIMS Bit

A. $4\frac{2}{7}$ 　　B. $7\frac{1}{2}$

C. $7\frac{5}{6}$ 　　D. $4\frac{1}{3}$

E. $8\frac{1}{2}$ 　　F. $8\frac{3}{4}$

L **Multiplying Fractions**

Multiply these fractions. Reduce answers to lowest terms. Estimate to see if your answers are reasonable.

A. $\frac{1}{2} \times \frac{1}{4} =$ 　　B. $\frac{1}{4} \times \frac{1}{4} =$

C. $\frac{2}{3} \times \frac{1}{2} =$ 　　D. $\frac{3}{8} \times \frac{1}{6} =$

E. $\frac{5}{8} \times \frac{2}{3} =$ 　　F. $\frac{1}{2} \times \frac{3}{5} =$

TIMS Task

A. $\frac{1}{8}$ 　　B. $\frac{1}{16}$

C. $\frac{2}{6} = \frac{1}{3}$ 　　D. $\frac{3}{48} = \frac{1}{16}$

E. $\frac{10}{24} = \frac{5}{12}$ 　　F. $\frac{3}{10}$

Student Questions	Teacher Notes

 Fact Practice

A. $60 \times 80 =$

B. $420 \div 70 =$

C. $32,000 \div 400 =$

D. $70 \times 8 =$

E. $2400 \div 6 =$

F. $7000 \times 40 =$

TIMS Bit

A. 4800

B. 6

C. 80

D. 560

E. 400

F. 280,000

 Inheriting Money

Krista's uncle died and left her his money. In order to claim her fortune, she has to solve this riddle which tells the amount she inherited.

Take your time to find a prime.
But, beware, it's one more than a square.
It's under one hundred and ends in seven.
Now, add six zeros and you'll be in heaven.
Problems, you say, there's more than one solution?
Then, add them, my dear, and enjoy your fortune.

How much money did Krista inherit?

TIMS Task

Primes less than 100 and one more than a square:

5, 17, and 37; 17 and 37 end in a 7; $17,000,000 + $37,000,000 = $54,000,000

LESSON GUIDE 1

Hexagon Duets

Estimated
Class
Sessions:
1–2

This lesson has two parts. In the first part,
students play a game using pattern blocks
to review addition of fractions and to
introduce addition of mixed numbers. So
that students can develop number sense with fractions, this game emphasizes finding sums using
manipulatives, rather than procedures.

In the second part of the lesson, students use pattern
blocks to explore renaming mixed numbers using
equivalent mixed numbers and fractions. They practice these skills which are prerequisites for adding
mixed numbers using paper-and-pencil methods.
The activities in Lesson 2 develop paper-and-pencil
methods for adding mixed numbers.

Key Content

- Adding fractions.
- Adding mixed numbers using pattern blocks.
- Renaming mixed numbers.

Curriculum Sequence

Before This Unit

In Grade 4 Unit 12 students used pattern blocks to model
addition and subtraction of fractions. In Grade 5 Unit 3
Lesson 2, they renamed mixed numbers as improper
fractions and improper fractions as mixed numbers using
pattern blocks. In Unit 5 Lessons 6 and 7, students used
rectangles on dot paper to model addition and subtraction
of fractions. In Unit 11 Lesson 6 students added and
subtracted fractions using common denominators and
they reduced fractions to lowest terms.

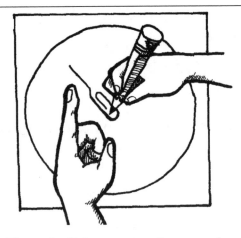

Figure 2: *Using a paper clip as a spinner*

 **TIMS Tip**

If clear plastic spinners are not available, students can use an
opened paper clip and a pencil as shown in Figure 2. Bobby
pins can also be used instead of paper clips.

Materials List

Print Materials for Students

	Math Facts and Daily Practice and Problems	Activity	Homework
Student Books			
Student Guide		*Hexagon Duets* Pages 376–379	*Hexagon Duets* Homework Section Page 379
Discovery Assignment Book		*Hexagon Duets Spinner* Page 193	
Teacher Resources			
Facts Resource Guide	DPP Item 12A		
Unit Resource Guide	DPP Items A–B Page 10		

available on Teacher Resource CD

All Transparency Masters, Blackline Masters, and Assessment Blackline Masters in the Unit Resource Guide are on the Teacher Resource CD.

Supplies for Each Student Pair

1 set of pattern blocks (at least 2–3 yellow hexagons, 6 red trapezoids, 10 blue rhombuses, 10 green triangles, 6 brown trapezoids, and 12 purple triangles)

Supplies for Each Student Group

1 spinner or paper clip and pencil

Materials for the Teacher

Transparency of *Hexagon Duets Spinner* Game Page (Discovery Assignment Book) Page 193, optional overhead pattern blocks, optional

Hexagon Duets

This game is played by four players, two players on each team.

Materials

Each group of four players needs:

- Pattern blocks
- Paper and pencil
- *Hexagon Duets Spinner* Game Page from the *Discovery Assignment Book,* four copies
- A clear, plastic spinner (or a paper clip and a pencil)

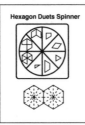

Hexagon Duets Spinner

Rules

- One yellow hexagon is one whole.
- Each player takes a turn. On your turn, spin the spinner twice. Each time you spin, place the pattern blocks on the outline of the two hexagons on your *Hexagon Duets Spinner* Game Page. Follow Jackie and Lin's example in Questions 1–3.
- Add the two fractions together. You may need to trade your pattern blocks for other pattern blocks to find the sum.
- Write a number sentence for the sum of your two fractions.
- Add your sum to your partner's sum to find a grand total. Write a number sentence for the grand total.
- The team with the largest total wins the round and earns $\frac{1}{3}$ of a point.
- Continue to play more rounds. The first team to earn one whole point is the winner.

***Student Guide* - Page 376**

Journal Prompt

While playing a round of *Hexagon Duets,* Alexis spun $\frac{1}{3}$ and $\frac{1}{12}$ and Manny spun $\frac{1}{6}$ and $\frac{1}{4}$. Will their team total be more than one or less than one? How do you know?

Discuss

Jackie and Lin are a team in a game of *Hexagon Duets.* In the first round of the game, Jackie spins $\frac{5}{6}$ and $\frac{1}{2}$. She adds her fractions together with pattern blocks. Then, she writes a number sentence.

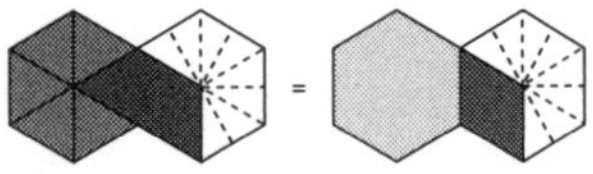

$\frac{5}{6} + \frac{1}{2} = 1\frac{1}{3}$

1. What pattern blocks did Jackie trade?

Lin spins $\frac{1}{6}$ and $\frac{2}{3}$. Here is her work.

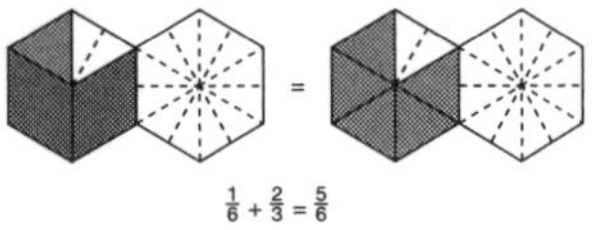

$\frac{1}{6} + \frac{2}{3} = \frac{5}{6}$

2. What pattern blocks did Lin trade?

To complete the round, the girls put their pieces together to find the grand total of their two sums.

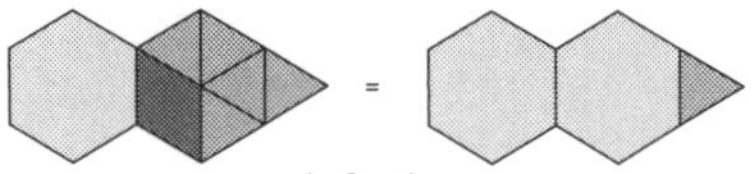

$1\frac{1}{3} + \frac{5}{6} = 2\frac{1}{6}$

3. The two players on the other team take their turns. Their grand total is $2\frac{1}{12}$. Did Jackie and Lin win the round? Why or why not?

***Student Guide* - Page 377**

Developing the Activity

Part 1. Playing *Hexagon Duets*

The game is played in groups of four, in which pairs of students form teams and play against the other pair. Before play begins, discuss the rules on the *Hexagon Duets* Activity Pages in the *Student Guide.* ***Questions 1–3*** highlight two important aspects of the game: representing addition problems using pattern blocks and writing number sentences for the resulting sums. To clarify the rules, play a sample round of the game with three students using overhead pattern blocks and a transparency of *Hexagon Duets Spinner* Game Page from the *Discovery Assignment Book.*

As students play the game, they need not find common denominators to find the sums or reduce their answers to lowest terms. They can simply use the pattern blocks to add and make trades until they can represent the sum as a proper fraction or a mixed number. Instead of concentrating on procedures at this point, encourage students to focus on the reasonableness of the results.

Ask:

- *Should the sums be less than one or more than one? Less than two or more than two?*

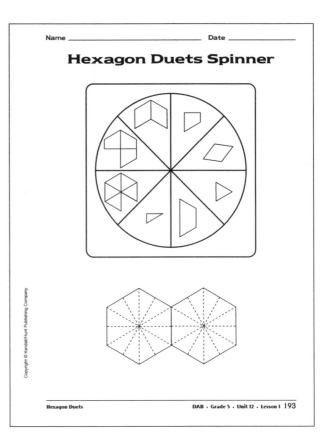

Name ______________________ Date ____________

Hexagon Duets Spinner

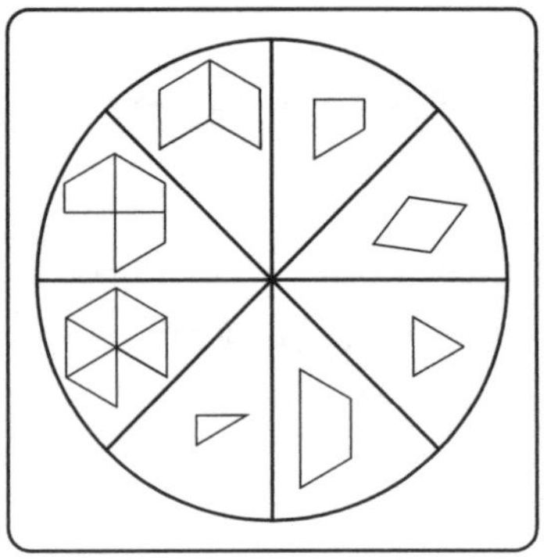

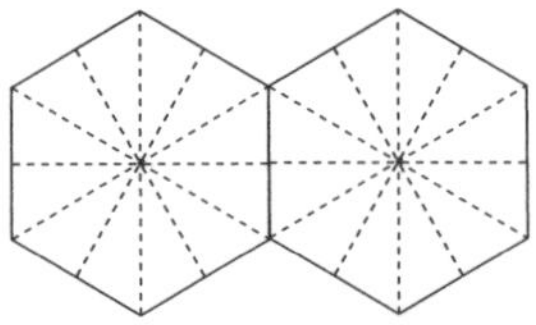

***Discovery Assignment Book* - Page 193**

Part 2. Many Names for Mixed Numbers

This part of the activity helps students find many equivalent representations of mixed numbers. Understanding equivalence is an important step in many procedures using fractions, including addition of mixed numbers.

Use pattern blocks to represent $2\frac{1}{3}$ as shown in the Many Names for Mixed Numbers section of the *Hexagon Duets* Activity Pages in the *Student Guide*. Ask students to follow your example using their pattern blocks. (They will need to work in groups of three or four in order to have enough blocks for some of the questions.) Once they have shown $2\frac{1}{3}$ with blocks, ask them to use the blocks to find as many fractions and mixed numbers as possible that are equivalent to $2\frac{1}{3}$ *(Question 4),* using only one or two colors of blocks in any one mixed number or improper fraction. Encourage students to write a number sentence that shows the equivalence of the various representations. Figure 3 shows five such representations for $2\frac{1}{3}$ as well as a proper number sentence.

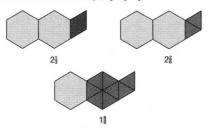

Many Names for Mixed Numbers

When using mixed numbers and fractions, you often need to use different names for the same mixed number. For example, $2\frac{1}{3} = 2\frac{2}{6} = 1\frac{8}{6}$.

$2\frac{1}{3}$ $2\frac{2}{6}$

$1\frac{8}{6}$

4. Find as many fractions and mixed numbers as you can that are equivalent to $2\frac{1}{3}$ that can be shown using pattern blocks. For this lesson, one yellow hexagon is one whole. You may use the yellow, red, blue, green, and purple blocks, but you may use no more than two colors of blocks. For any number, be prepared to show the class your solutions using pattern blocks and number sentences.

Work with your group to answer Questions 5–6. Share pattern blocks. Follow these directions:

• Find as many mixed numbers and improper fractions as you can that are equivalent to the number in the problem. You must be able to show the mixed number or fraction with no more than two colors of pattern blocks.
• Write number sentences for your solutions. Follow the example for $2\frac{1}{3}$ above.

5. $3\frac{1}{4}$

6. 2

In Questions 7–9 you are given a mixed number or an improper fraction. Show this number with pattern blocks as it is written in the problem. Then, show it using only two colors and the fewest pieces possible. Write the mixed number represented by the pattern blocks when you use the fewest pieces.

378 SG · Grade 5 · Unit 12 · Lesson 1   **Hexagon Duets**

Student Guide - Page 378

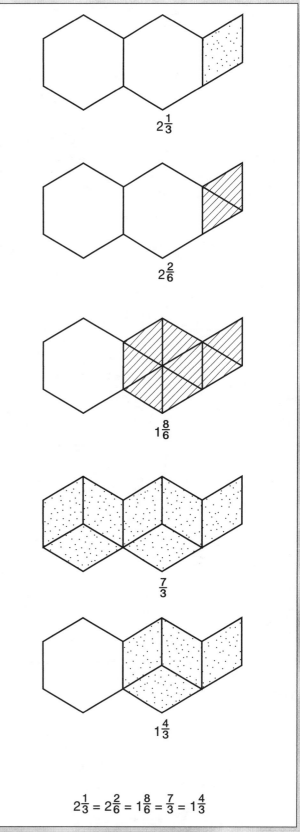

$$2\frac{1}{3} = 2\frac{2}{6} = 1\frac{8}{6} = \frac{7}{3} = 1\frac{4}{3}$$

Figure 3: *Five names for $2\frac{1}{3}$*

Use **Question 5** to guide students through the same procedure for $3\frac{1}{4}$. Remind students that they may use at most two colors of blocks to represent the mixed numbers. **Question 6** asks students to follow the same directions and to find different representations for a whole number. Figure 4 shows three ways to represent the number 2 using pattern blocks: $2 = \frac{4}{2} = 1\frac{4}{4}$.

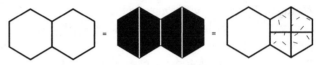

Figure 4: *Three names for 2:* $2 = \frac{4}{2} = 1\frac{4}{4}$

Questions 7–9 ask students to represent improper fractions and mixed numbers with pattern blocks. First, students represent the fraction as it is written in the problem. Then, they show the fraction using only two colors and the fewest pieces possible. They write the mixed numbers represented by the pattern blocks using the fewest pieces. Following these restrictions forces students to write mixed numbers with proper fractions in lowest terms. For example, to represent $1\frac{15}{6}$ with two colors and the fewest pieces, we must use yellow and red pieces. As shown in Figure 5, $1\frac{15}{6} = 3\frac{1}{2}$. A different example is shown in the *Student Guide*.

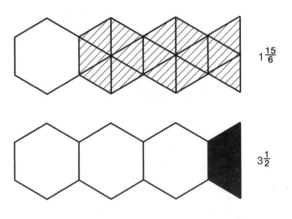

Figure 5: $1\frac{15}{6} = 3\frac{1}{2}$

Questions 10–12 provide practice renaming mixed numbers and improper fractions that cannot be modeled with pattern blocks.

Suggestions for Teaching the Lesson

Math Facts

DPP Bit A reviews the last six division facts.

Homework and Practice

- The Homework section in the *Student Guide* provides practice renaming mixed numbers. This section also provides practice solving problems involving fractions.

- Assign DPP Challenge B which involves making and understanding scale maps and using ratios to solve problems.

Assessment

- Use the Journal Prompt from Part 1 in the *Unit Resource Guide* to assess students' abilities to estimate sums of fractions.

- Use *Question 1* of the Homework section to assess students' abilities to rename mixed numbers.

Daily Practice and Problems: Challenge for Lesson 1

B. Challenge: Making a Map
(URG p. 10)

Frank made a map of his classroom. 1 cm on his map represents 50 centimeters in the classroom. He drew a straight line on his map from the teacher's desk to the garbage can. Then, he drew a straight line from the garbage can to the door. He made these measurements:

- The distance from the teacher's desk to the garbage can is 2.4 cm.

- The distance from the garbage can to the door is 4.6 cm.

Use Frank's measurements to predict the actual distance in the classroom from Mr. Moreno's desk to the garbage can, and then to the door.

Example: $1\frac{6}{4}$

Solution:

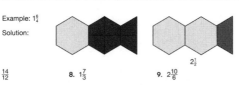

$2\frac{1}{2}$

7. $\frac{14}{12}$ 8. $1\frac{7}{3}$ 9. $2\frac{10}{6}$

In Questions 10–12 write each number as a mixed number with the fraction in lowest terms. There should be no improper fractions in your answers.

10. $\frac{15}{10}$ 11. $1\frac{17}{8}$ 12. $3\frac{14}{6}$

Homework

1. Write each number as a mixed number with the fraction in lowest terms. There should be no improper fractions in your answers.

   A. $\frac{15}{12}$ B. $2\frac{15}{20}$ C. $1\frac{10}{3}$

   D. $3\frac{12}{8}$ E. $5\frac{16}{6}$ F. $2\frac{18}{15}$

2. David is filling boxes with candy. One box holds $\frac{3}{8}$ pound and the other holds $\frac{1}{2}$ pound. He has 1 pound of candy. Does he have enough candy to completely fill both boxes? How do you know?

3. Jackie is sewing a skirt. The instructions call for $\frac{5}{8}$ yard of material. She bought $\frac{3}{4}$ yard. How much material will she have left over after she makes the skirt?

4. Nicholas lives $1\frac{3}{4}$ miles from school. Alexis lives $1\frac{7}{10}$ miles from school. Who lives farther from school? Justify your answer.

5. Jessie found a piece of wood that is 7 inches long. She needs a piece $6\frac{3}{8}$ inches long. How much wood will be left if she cuts off $6\frac{3}{8}$ inches?

6. Write all answers in lowest terms.

   A. $\frac{7}{8} + \frac{7}{8} =$ B. $\frac{5}{6} - \frac{1}{4} =$

   C. $\frac{4}{5} + \frac{7}{10} =$ D. $\frac{11}{12} + \frac{2}{3} =$

Hexagon Duets   SG · Grade 5 · Unit 12 · Lesson 1   379

Student Guide - Page 379

AT A GLANCE

Math Facts and Daily Practice and Problems

DPP Bit A reviews the last six division facts. Challenge B involves scale maps and using ratios to solve problems.

Part 1. Playing *Hexagon Duets*

1. Students read and discuss the rules for the game on the *Hexagon Duets* Activity Pages in the *Student Guide.*
2. Students read and discuss the example of a round of play in the *Student Guide* and answer *Questions 1–3.*
3. Students play the game using pattern blocks, a spinner, and the *Hexagon Duets Spinner* Game Page from the *Discovery Assignment Book.*

Part 2. Many Names for Mixed Numbers

1. Students find equivalent representations for mixed numbers using pattern blocks. *(Questions 4–9)*
2. Students find equivalent representations for mixed numbers using pencil and paper. *(Questions 10–12)*

Homework

Assign the Homework section in the *Student Guide.*

Assessment

1. Use the Journal Prompt as an assessment.
2. Use *Question 1* of the Homework section to assess renaming mixed numbers.

Notes:

Student Guide

Questions 1–12 (SG pp. 377–379)

1. Jackie traded 5 green triangles and 1 red trapezoid for 1 yellow hexagon and 1 blue rhombus.

2. Lin traded 1 green triangle and 2 blue rhombuses for 5 green triangles.

3. Yes, $2\frac{1}{6} > 2\frac{1}{12}$.

4. *See Figure 3 in Lesson Guide 1.

5. Answers will vary. Possible solutions include:
   $3\frac{1}{4} = 2\frac{5}{4} = 3\frac{3}{12} = \frac{13}{4}$

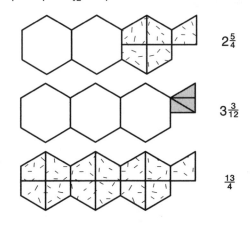

$2\frac{5}{4}$

$3\frac{3}{12}$

$\frac{13}{4}$

6. *See Figure 4 in Lesson Guide 1.

7.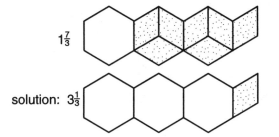

$\frac{14}{12}$ solution: $1\frac{1}{6}$

8.

$1\frac{7}{3}$

solution: $3\frac{1}{3}$

9.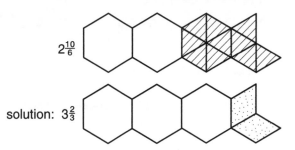

$2\frac{10}{6}$

solution: $3\frac{2}{3}$

10. $1\frac{1}{2}$

11. $3\frac{1}{8}$

12. $5\frac{1}{3}$

Homework (SG p. 379)

Questions 1–6

1. A. $1\frac{1}{4}$

   B. $2\frac{3}{4}$

   C. $4\frac{1}{3}$

   D. $4\frac{1}{2}$

   E. $7\frac{2}{3}$

   F. $3\frac{1}{5}$

2. Yes; the two boxes together hold $\frac{3}{8} + \frac{1}{2} = \frac{7}{8}$ pound of candy. Since David has 1 pound of candy, he has enough candy to fill the two boxes.

3. $\frac{1}{8}$ yard

4. Nicholas. Students' justifications will vary.

5. $\frac{5}{8}$ inch

6. A. $\frac{7}{4}$ or $1\frac{3}{4}$

   B. $\frac{7}{12}$

   C. $\frac{3}{2}$ or $1\frac{1}{2}$

   D. $\frac{19}{12}$ or $1\frac{7}{12}$

*Answers and/or discussion are included in the Lesson Guide.

**Answers for all the Home Practice in the *Discovery Assignment Book* are at the end of the unit.

Daily Practice and Problems:
Bit for Lesson 2

C. Do You See a Triangle?

(URG p. 11)

In each case, tell whether the given lengths will make a triangle. Justify your answer. (*Hint:* Estimation is an appropriate strategy for solving this problem.)

A. 3 inches, 4 inches, 6 inches

B. $3\frac{1}{2}$ inches, 8 inches, $4\frac{5}{8}$ inches

C. $15\frac{3}{16}$ inches, $7\frac{1}{4}$ inches, $7\frac{3}{8}$ inches

---

DPP Challenge is on page 28. Suggestions for using the DPPs are on page 28.

LESSON GUIDE 2

Adding Mixed Numbers

Estimated Class Sessions: 1

Students use pattern blocks to model the addition of mixed numbers and develop paper-and-pencil procedures.

Key Content

- Adding mixed numbers using paper and pencil.
- Reducing fractions to lowest terms.
- Estimating sums of mixed numbers.

Curriculum Sequence

Before This Unit

Students converted improper fractions to mixed numbers in Unit 3 Lesson 2. They reviewed using common denominators to add fractions with paper and pencil in Unit 11 Lesson 6.

Materials List

Print Materials for Students

	Math Facts and Daily Practice and Problems	Activity	Homework
Student Books			
Student Guide		*Adding Mixed Numbers* Pages 380–382	*Adding Mixed Numbers* Homework Section Page 382
Discovery Assignment Book			Home Practice Parts 1 & 2 Page 189
Teacher Resource			
Unit Resource Guide	DPP Items C–D Page 11 ⊙		

⊙ *available on Teacher Resource CD*

All Transparency Masters, Blackline Masters, and Assessment Blackline Masters in the Unit Resource Guide are on the Teacher Resource CD.

Supplies for Each Student Pair

1 set of pattern blocks (at least 2–3 yellow hexagons, 6 red trapezoids, 10 blue rhombuses, 10 green triangles, 6 brown trapezoids, and 12 purple triangles)

Materials for the Teacher

overhead pattern blocks, optional

TIMS Tip

Students should work in pairs in order to share pattern blocks.

Developing the Activity

Briefly review the addition of fractions by using pattern blocks as a model. Figure 6 shows one way to add $\frac{2}{3}$ and $\frac{1}{2}$ using pattern blocks. Note that finding the common denominator (6) is modeled by finding one color (green) to cover both addends. Other strategies of combining the blocks are also possible.

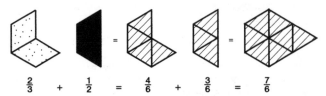

$$\frac{2}{3} \quad + \quad \frac{1}{2} \quad = \quad \frac{4}{6} \quad + \quad \frac{3}{6} \quad = \quad \frac{7}{6}$$

Figure 6: *Finding common denominators using pattern blocks to find common colors of blocks*

Remind students to check for the reasonableness of their answers. Ask:

- *Should the answer be more or less than $\frac{1}{2}$? More or less than 1?*

Have students use pattern blocks to add mixed numbers using these examples:

$$2\frac{1}{6} + 1\frac{1}{3}$$
$$1\frac{1}{2} + 2\frac{3}{4}$$

Discuss strategies. Students can find a common denominator by covering all the fractional pieces with pieces of one color. Another strategy for adding $1\frac{1}{2} + 2\frac{3}{4}$ is shown in Figure 7.

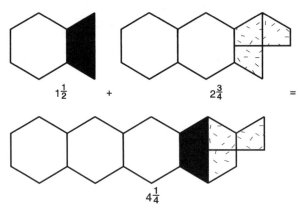

Figure 7: *Adding $1\frac{1}{2} + 2\frac{3}{4}$*

Have students use pencil and paper to do the same problems. Students can rely on skills they have used previously to add fractions. The only new aspect here is that we have wholes as well as fractional pieces. The problem $1\frac{1}{2} + 2\frac{3}{4}$ is discussed in

the *Student Guide.* After students have shared their own strategies, they can read the discussion of this problem on the *Adding Mixed Numbers* Activity Pages in the *Student Guide* and compare strategies. Discuss the last step. Since the mixed number $3\frac{5}{4}$ contains an improper fraction, it is rewritten as $4\frac{1}{4}$ ($3\frac{5}{4} = 3 + 1\frac{1}{4} = 4\frac{1}{4}$).

The questions in the Explore section give students practice adding mixed numbers with and without pattern blocks. Students should work on the problems in *Question 1* in pairs using pattern blocks. The problems in *Question 2* cannot be solved using pattern blocks. Use these problems as examples to show students generalized procedures for adding mixed numbers. Students may choose to add the fractions first, then change any improper fractions in the sum to mixed numbers. Or, students may choose to change the mixed numbers to improper fractions before they add.

Question 3 asks students to describe a method for adding mixed numbers. No matter what strategy students choose, encourage them to check to see if their answers are reasonable and that they have left no improper fractions in their final answers.

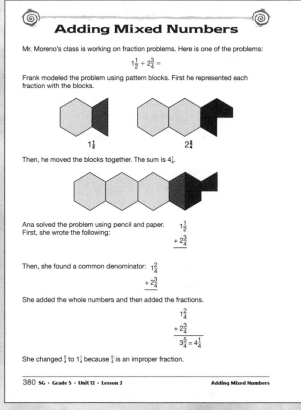

Student Guide - Page 380

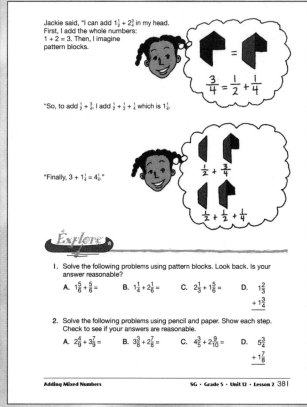

Student Guide - Page 381

Daily Practice and Problems: Challenge for Lesson 2

D. Challenge: Making a Quilt
(URG p. 11)

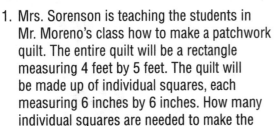

1. Mrs. Sorenson is teaching the students in Mr. Moreno's class how to make a patchwork quilt. The entire quilt will be a rectangle measuring 4 feet by 5 feet. The quilt will be made up of individual squares, each measuring 6 inches by 6 inches. How many individual squares are needed to make the quilt? Explain how you solved the problem.

2. There are 22 students in Mr. Moreno's class. The students are going to cut the individual squares from scraps of material. How many individual squares should each student cut out in order to have enough squares for the quilt?

---

3. Describe a method for adding mixed numbers. You may need to use some of these words: equivalent, common denominator, mixed number, improper fraction, and lowest terms. You can use $1\frac{1}{2} + 2\frac{5}{8}$ as an example to help explain this method.

Homework

Solve the following problems using paper and pencil or mental math. Reduce all fractions to lowest terms. Do not leave any improper fractions in your answers.

1. $2 + 4\frac{3}{5} =$ 2. $4\frac{3}{4} + 1\frac{5}{6} =$ 3. $1\frac{7}{10} + 3\frac{1}{2} =$

4. Solve the problem in Question 3 another way. Explain both of your strategies.

5. $5\frac{2}{3} + 3\frac{1}{12} =$ 6. $3\frac{4}{5} + 2\frac{1}{5} =$ 7. $7\frac{1}{5}$ 8. $4\frac{3}{5}$
                                              $+ 2\frac{1}{10}$ $+ 5\frac{3}{4}$

9. Look back at your answer to Question 8. Is it reasonable? Should it be more than 10 or less than 10? Explain.

10. Lee Yah spent $6\frac{1}{2}$ hours in school and $1\frac{3}{4}$ hours doing her homework. What is the total time she spent at school and on her homework?

11. A recipe calls for $1\frac{1}{3}$ cups of whole wheat flour and $2\frac{3}{4}$ cups of white flour. How many cups of flour are needed?

12. Nicholas checked the odometer in the car when he got a ride to school. His route to school is 1.3 miles. His soccer coach told him that it is a mile and a half from school to the practice field. How far does Nicholas have to walk to get from home to school to soccer practice?

13. A. A customer bought $2\frac{1}{3}$ yards of print material and $2\frac{3}{4}$ yards of solid color material. How many yards did the customer buy?
   B. Both kinds of material cost $3.00 a yard. The customer has $15. Is this enough money to buy the material? Explain.

14. Jessie is making a bird house. She needs 2 boards which measure $1\frac{3}{4}$ feet each and a board which measures $1\frac{1}{2}$ feet long. She has one board which is 4 feet long. Can she cut the 3 shorter boards from the longer one? Why or why not?

382 SG · Grade 5 · Unit 12 · Lesson 2   **Adding Mixed Numbers**

Student Guide - Page 382

Suggestions for Teaching the Lesson

Homework and Practice

- Before assigning the homework, check to see if students are comfortable with solving problems written both horizontally and vertically by noting student progress as they work on *Questions 1–2* in the Explore section. Encourage students to use the example problem in the *Student Guide* to help them solve the problems in the Homework section.

- Assign DPP item C. Bit C reviews geometry concepts including side lengths of triangles and requires estimating sums of fractions.

- Assign Parts 1 and 2 of the Home Practice which provide practice with multiplication and division. Students will need a calculator for Part 2.

Answers for Parts 1 and 2 of the Home Practice can be found in the Answer Key at the end of this lesson and at the end of this unit.

Assessment

Use *Questions 3–4* in the Homework section to assess student abilities to add mixed numbers using more than one strategy and to explain their thinking.

Extension

DPP Challenge D extends students' fluency with geometric concepts involving measurement and area of squares.

Name _____ Date _____

Unit 12: Home Practice

Part 1 Multiplication and Division Practice

Use a paper and pencil method to solve the following problems. Write any remainders as fractions in lowest terms.

1. A. $8967 ÷ 6 =$ B. $5875 ÷ 50 =$

    C. $246 × 9 =$ D. $2400 ÷ 30 =$

    E. $105 × 4 =$

2. Can you solve any of the above problems using mental math? If so, explain your strategies.

Part 2 Division Practice

1. Solve the following problems in your head or with paper and pencil. Write the quotient as a mixed number. Reduce all fractions to lowest terms.

    A. $33 ÷ 4 =$ B. $76 ÷ 9 =$ C. $17 ÷ 2 =$

    D. $108 ÷ 10 =$ E. $54 ÷ 7 =$ F. $41 ÷ 6 =$

    G. $42 ÷ 8 =$ H. $23 ÷ 6 =$ I. $67 ÷ 8 =$

2. Use a calculator to find the answers to the following. Write your answers as mixed numbers. Reduce all fractions to lowest terms.

    A. $1388 ÷ 16 =$ B. $18,478 ÷ 24 =$ C. $43,956 ÷ 32 =$

USING FRACTIONS   DAB · Grade 5 · Unit 12   189

Copyright © Kendall/Hunt Publishing Company

Discovery Assignment Book - Page 189

AT A GLANCE

Math Facts and Daily Practice and Problems

DPP Bit C reviews geometry concepts and estimating sums of fractions. DPP item D challenges students to solve a problem about quilts.

Developing the Activity

1. Briefly review the addition of fractions using pattern blocks and using paper and pencil.

2. Have students use pattern blocks to add mixed numbers, using these examples.

   $2\frac{1}{6} + 1\frac{1}{3}$

   $1\frac{1}{2} + 2\frac{3}{4}$

3. Have students use pencil and paper to do the same problems. Discuss strategies.

4. Students read the discussion on the *Adding Mixed Numbers* Activity Pages in the *Student Guide.*

5. Students practice adding mixed numbers using pattern blocks in *Question 1* and without pattern blocks in *Question 2* of the *Adding Mixed Numbers* Activity Pages in the *Student Guide.*

6. Students articulate a general method for adding mixed numbers. *(Question 3)*

Homework

1. Assign the homework problems in the *Student Guide.*
2. Assign Parts 1–2 of the Home Practice.

Assessment

Use *Questions 3–4* of the Homework section as an assessment.

Notes:

Student Guide

Questions 1–3 (SG pp. 381–382)

1. **A.** $2\frac{2}{3}$

   B. $3\frac{5}{12}$

   C. $4\frac{1}{6}$

   D. $3\frac{5}{12}$

2. **A.** $6\frac{2}{9}$

   B. $6\frac{1}{4}$

   C. $7\frac{1}{2}$

   D. $7\frac{5}{8}$

3. Answers will vary. The common denominator for the fractions $\frac{1}{2}$ and $\frac{5}{6}$ is 12. Find equivalent fractions with denominator 12. $\frac{1}{2}$ is equivalent to $\frac{6}{12}$ and $\frac{5}{6}$ is equivalent to $\frac{10}{12}$. Add the whole numbers 1 and 2 to get 3. Now, add the fractions $\frac{6}{12}$ and $\frac{10}{12}$ to get $\frac{16}{12}$. Converting this to mixed numbers, we get $1\frac{4}{12}$. Adding this to 3 we get $4\frac{4}{12}$. Reducing to lowest terms the answer is $4\frac{1}{3}$.

Homework (SG p. 382)

Questions 1–14

1. $6\frac{3}{5}$

2. $6\frac{7}{12}$

3. $5\frac{1}{5}$

4. Two possible solutions: $1\frac{7}{10} = 1\frac{7}{10}$, $3\frac{1}{2} = 3\frac{5}{10}$, $4\frac{12}{10} = 5\frac{2}{10} = 5\frac{1}{5}$; Add the whole numbers first: $1 + 3 = 4$. Then, add the fractions. Think of $\frac{7}{10}$ as $\frac{5}{10} + \frac{2}{10}$ or $\frac{1}{2} + \frac{2}{10}$. Then, $\frac{7}{10} + \frac{1}{2} = \frac{1}{2} + \frac{2}{10} + \frac{1}{2}$ or $1\frac{2}{10}$. So, $4 + 1\frac{2}{10} = 5\frac{2}{10} = 5\frac{1}{5}$

5. $8\frac{3}{4}$

6. 6

7. $9\frac{3}{10}$

8. $10\frac{7}{20}$

9. More than 10; the whole numbers add up to 9 and the fractions add up to more than 1.

10. $8\frac{1}{4}$ hours

11. $4\frac{1}{12}$ cups

12. 2.8 miles or $2\frac{4}{5}$ miles

13. **A.** $5\frac{1}{12}$ yards

    B. No; since the material costs $3.00 per yard, the customer can only buy 5 yards with $15. The total amount of material is more than 5 yards, so the customer won't have enough money.

14. No. $1\frac{3}{4} + 1\frac{3}{4} = 3\frac{1}{2}$ ft. $3\frac{1}{2} + 1\frac{1}{2} > 4$ ft.

Discovery Assignment Book

**Home Practice (DAB p. 189)

Part 1. Multiplication and Division Practice

Questions 1–2

1. **A.** $1494\frac{1}{2}$

   B. $117\frac{1}{2}$

   C. 2214

   D. 80

   E. 420

2. Answers will vary:
   Possible response for 1E:
   $105 \times 4 = 100 \times 4 + 5 \times 4 = 400 + 20 = 420$

Part 2. Division Practice

Questions 1–2

1. **A.** $8\frac{1}{4}$ **B.** $8\frac{4}{9}$

   C. $8\frac{1}{2}$ **D.** $10\frac{8}{10} = 10\frac{4}{5}$

   E. $7\frac{5}{7}$ **F.** $6\frac{5}{6}$

   G. $5\frac{2}{8} = 5\frac{1}{4}$ **H.** $3\frac{5}{6}$

   I. $8\frac{3}{8}$

2. **A.** $86\frac{12}{16} = 86\frac{3}{4}$

   B. $769\frac{22}{24} = 769\frac{11}{12}$

   C. $1373\frac{20}{32} = 1373\frac{5}{8}$

*Answers and/or discussion are included in the Lesson Guide.

**Answers for all the Home Practice in the *Discovery Assignment Book* are at the end of the unit.

LESSON GUIDE 3

Fractions of Groups

Estimated Class Sessions: 1

By using diagrams, students find the product of a fraction and a whole number. They also look for patterns in multiplication problems and use the patterns to estimate the size of the products. This lesson helps develop a conceptual understanding of multiplication with fractions and further develops number sense. Students will use paper-and-pencil procedures for multiplication of fractions in Lesson 5.

Key Content

- Multiplying a fraction and a whole number using diagrams.
- Using patterns to build number sense.

Materials List

Print Materials for Students

	Math Facts and Daily Practice and Problems	Activity	Homework
Student Book — Student Guide		*Fractions of Groups* Pages 383–385	*Fractions of Groups* Homework Section Pages 385–386
Teacher Resources — Facts Resource Guide	DPP Item 12E		
Teacher Resources — Unit Resource Guide	DPP Items E–F Page 12		

available on Teacher Resource CD

All Transparency Masters, Blackline Masters, and Assessment Blackline Masters in the Unit Resource Guide are on the Teacher Resource CD.

Fractions of Groups

Johnny Appleseed Apple Company sells gift boxes. The small gift boxes have
12 apples and the large gift boxes have 24 apples.

1. If one-fourth of the apples in each gift box are yellow,
   A. How many apples in the small gift box are yellow?
   B. How many apples in the large gift box are yellow?

2. A. In the fraction $\frac{1}{4}$, what information does the denominator give you?
   B. What information does the numerator give you?
   C. What other information do you need in order to know the number of apples in $\frac{1}{4}$ of a box?
   D. What is the difference between $\frac{1}{4}$ and $\frac{4}{1}$?

3. Write number sentences for the following:
   A. Four groups of three apples make 12 apples in all.
   B. Four groups of six apples make 24 apples in all.
   C. What operation did you use in your number sentences?

Lin used the diagram and number sentence shown here to
represent one-fourth of the apples in the large box. Both her
diagram and number sentence represent one-fourth of a
group of 24 apples. We write this as: $\frac{1}{4} \times 24 = 6$ apples.

$\frac{1}{4} \times 24 = 6$ apples

4. Draw a diagram similar to Lin's. Show the following using your diagram and write a number sentence for each:
   A. One-fourth of a group of 24 apples.
   B. Two-fourths of a group of 24 apples.
   C. Three-fourths of a group of 24 apples.
   D. Four-fourths of a group of 24 apples.

Fractions of Groups   SG · Grade 5 · Unit 12 · Lesson 3   383

Student Guide - Page 383

Content Note

Note that while the word "of" often implies multiplication,
it is important not to overgeneralize. For example, the
problems below use the word "of" but are solved without
multiplication:

Six of the students in Mr. Moreno's class are learning to
play instruments, and eight of his students are in the
chorus. How many are studying music?

If there are 22 students in Mr. Moreno's class, what fraction
of the students are learning to play an instrument?

Developing the Activity

In previous units, students explored fractions using
area models (rectangles on dot paper and pattern
blocks) and a number line model (fractohoppers). In
this lesson, students work with fractions of sets of
discrete objects. For example, students find the fraction of red apples in a box of 12 apples. The whole is
a group of 12 discrete objects. The sequence of discussion questions develops the fraction concepts
involved in multiplying a fraction and a whole number. Arrays of apples in gift boxes of different sizes
provide the context.

Students investigate the concept of a whole in
Questions 1–2. Just as the size of a fraction using an
area model depends on the area of the whole, the size
of a fraction of a set of discrete objects depends on
the number of objects in the whole set. First, students
find the number of apples in two different-sized gift
boxes. One-fourth of the apples in a box of 12 apples
is three apples *(Question 1A),* while one-fourth of a
box of 24 apples is six apples *(Question 1B).*

Question 2 reviews the terms numerator and denominator. For the fraction $\frac{1}{4}$, the 4 in the denominator tells
us to divide the 12 apples into four equal groups. The
1 in the numerator tells us that we are interested in
one of the groups. To know the number of apples
in $\frac{1}{4}$ of a box of apples, it is essential to know the
number of apples in the whole box *(Question 2C).*
To show the difference between the fractions $\frac{1}{4}$ and $\frac{4}{1}$
(Question 2D), we can apply the definitions of
numerator and denominator to $\frac{4}{1}$. For the fraction $\frac{4}{1}$,
the 1 in the denominator tells us that all of the apples
in the whole set are in one group. The 4 in the numerator means that we are interested in 4 whole groups,
so $\frac{4}{1}$ is equivalent to 4 whole boxes.

Questions 3–5 emphasize the language used in
multiplication sentences. A number sentence for
"Four groups of 6 apples makes 24 apples in all"
is $4 \times 6 = 24$. Similarly, a number sentence for
"One-fourth of a group of 24 apples is 6 apples"
is $\frac{1}{4} \times 24 = 6$. You may wish to ask students to
write number sentences for the following:

• *How many players are on 8 teams of 11 players
  each?* $(8 \times 11 = 88)$

• *One-half of a class of 22 students goes home for
  lunch. How many students go home for lunch?*
  $(\frac{1}{2} \times 22 = 11)$

Questions 6–7 develop students' number sense so that they will be able to estimate the product of a fraction and a whole number. Students use diagrams to complete the table in Figure 8.

Multiplication Number Sentences
$\frac{1}{3} \times 12 = 4$
$\frac{2}{3} \times 12 = 8$
$\frac{3}{3} \times 12 = 12$
$\frac{4}{3} \times 12 = 16$
$\frac{5}{3} \times 12 = 20$
$\frac{6}{3} \times 12 = 24$

Figure 8: *Completed table for Question 6*

A diagram is used in the *Student Guide* to solve the problem $\frac{4}{3} \times 12 = 16$. Ask students if they can solve the problem another way. They may see that since $\frac{4}{3}$ equals $1\frac{1}{3}$, the problem can be rewritten as $1\frac{1}{3} \times 12$. Remind students that $1\frac{1}{3}$ can be thought of as 1 and $\frac{1}{3}$ or $1 + \frac{1}{3}$. Using the context of the apple gift boxes, we can find the number of apples in one whole box (12) and the number of apples in $\frac{1}{3}$ of a box (4) and reason that one and one-third boxes of apples is $12 + 4$ or 16 apples.

To complete the row for $\frac{5}{3} \times 12$, students can draw a diagram similar to the one in Figure 9 which shows two whole sets of 12 apples. Each set is divided into three groups, and five of the groups are circled, so $\frac{5}{3} \times 12 = 20$.

Question 7A asks students to look for patterns in the table. Possible student responses include the following:

- As the fraction gets larger, the product gets larger.
- You can find the products by skip counting by fours since $\frac{1}{3}$ of 12 is 4.
- When the fraction is less than one, the product is less than 12.
- When the fraction is greater than one, the product is greater than 12.

Question 7C asks students when the product of a fraction and 12 is equal to 12. The product is equal to 12 when the fraction is $\frac{3}{3}$ or 1. This is because multiplying a number by one results in the same number.

---

5. A. What patterns do you see in the number sentences?
   B. What is another name for $\frac{4}{3}$? Write another number sentence for Question 4D using this name.

John used this diagram to show one-third of a small box of apples.

 $\frac{1}{3} \times 12 = 4$ apples

He used this diagram to show four-thirds of a small box of apples.

 $\frac{4}{3} \times 12 = 16$ apples

6. Copy the following chart on your paper. Complete the chart following the example in the first row. (Remember, the answer to a multiplication problem is a **product**. For example, 4 is the product of $\frac{1}{3} \times 12$.)

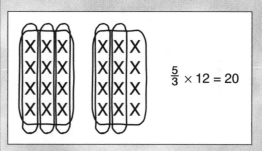

Multiplication Number Sentences
$\frac{1}{3} \times 12 = 4$
$\frac{2}{3} \times 12 =$
$\frac{3}{3} \times 12 =$
$\frac{4}{3} \times 12 = 16$
$\frac{5}{3} \times 12 =$
$\frac{6}{3} \times 12 =$

7. A. Describe the patterns you see in the table.
   B. When is the product less than 12? Why?
   C. When is the product equal to 12? Why?
   D. When is the product greater than 12? Why?

Fractions of Groups

Student Guide - Page 384

 $\frac{5}{3} \times 12 = 20$

Figure 9: *A diagram for $\frac{5}{3} \times 12 = 20$*

📓 **Journal Prompt**
If you multiply a fraction and a whole number, when will the product be greater than the whole number? When will the product be less than the whole number?

F. Task: Practicing the Operations
(URG p. 12)

Use paper and pencil to solve the following problems. Estimate to be sure your answers are reasonable. For A and B, write your answer (the quotient) as a mixed number. Fractions should be in lowest terms.

1. A. $636 \div 16 =$

   B. $1994 \div 8 =$

   C. $467 \times 8 =$

   D. $37.2 + 125.06 =$

   E. $1045.35 - 76.3 =$

   F. $0.7 \times 85 =$

2. Explain your estimation strategy for 1F.

Suggestions for Teaching the Lesson

Math Facts

DPP item E reviews the last six division facts using multiples of 10.

Homework and Practice

- The Homework section in the *Student Guide* reviews the concepts developed in the discussion questions. Encourage students to use both diagrams and number sentences as part of their solutions.

- Assign DPP Task F which reviews computation.

Assessment

Use **Question 7** in the Homework section to assess students' understanding of the concepts and their abilities to find the product of a fraction and a whole number.

---

8. Draw a diagram and write a number sentence for each problem.

   A. $\frac{1}{4} \times 12$ B. $\frac{2}{4} \times 12$ C. $\frac{3}{4} \times 12$

   D. $\frac{4}{4} \times 12$ E. $\frac{5}{4} \times 12$ F. $\frac{6}{4} \times 12$

Homework

Solve the following problems. Draw a diagram and write a number sentence for each problem. Follow the example.

Example: Edward gave $\frac{2}{3}$ of a small box of apples to his grandmother. How many apples did he give her?

$$\frac{2}{3} \times 12 = 8$$

Remember, there are 12 apples in a small box and 24 apples in a large box.

1. A. One-half of the apples in the small box of apples are red. How many are red?
   B. One-fourth of the apples in the small box are green. How many are green?

2. Nila's family received a large box of apples.
   A. Nila ate $\frac{1}{8}$ of the apples. How many apples did Nila eat?
   B. Nila's father took $\frac{5}{8}$ of the apples to work to share with his co-workers. How many apples did he take to work?

3. For each problem, decide how many apples each person ate.
   A. Manny ate $\frac{1}{3}$ of a large box of apples.
   B. Blanca ate $\frac{1}{8}$ of the apples in a large box.
   C. Michael ate $\frac{3}{4}$ of the apples in a small box.
   D. Romesh ate $\frac{5}{8}$ of the apples in a small box.

Student Guide - Page 385

---

4. Muffy's Muffins are sold in packages of eight. Complete the following table:

Multiplication Number Sentences
$\frac{1}{4} \times 8 = 2$
$\frac{2}{4} \times 8 =$
$\frac{3}{4} \times 8 =$
$\frac{4}{4} \times 8 =$
$\frac{5}{4} \times 8 =$
$\frac{6}{4} \times 8 =$

5. A. Describe the patterns you see in the table.
   B. When is the product equal to the number of muffins in the whole package? Why?
   C. When is the product less than the number of muffins in the whole package? Why?
   D. When is the product more than the number of muffins in the whole package? Why?
   E. What is another name for $\frac{6}{4}$? Rewrite a number sentence from your chart using this name.

6. Lee Yah's friends ate $1\frac{1}{2}$ packages of Muffy's Muffins. How many muffins did they eat?

7. Solve the following problems.

   A. $\frac{1}{10} \times 20 =$ B. $\frac{1}{5} \times 20 =$

   C. $\frac{1}{4} \times 20 =$ D. $\frac{1}{2} \times 20 =$

   E. $\frac{3}{5} \times 20 =$ F. $\frac{3}{4} \times 20 =$

   G. $\frac{9}{10} \times 20 =$ H. $1\frac{1}{2} \times 20 =$

Student Guide - Page 386

AT A GLANCE

Math Facts and Daily Practice and Problems

DPP Bit E reviews the last six division facts. Task F reviews computation with whole numbers and decimals.

Developing the Activity

Use *Questions 1–8* in the *Student Guide* to lead a class discussion that explores the concepts needed to multiply a fraction and a whole number.

Homework

Assign the Homework section in the *Student Guide.*

Assessment

Use *Question 7* in the Homework section as an assessment.

Notes:

Student Guide

Questions 1–8 (SG pp. 383–385)

1. **A.** *3 apples

   B. *6 apples

2.* **A.** *The 4 in the denominator tells us to divide the whole into 4 equal groups.

   B. *The 1 in the numerator tells us that we are interested in 1 of the 4 groups.

   C. *The number of apples in a whole box.

   D. *$\frac{1}{4}$ means that the whole set is divided into 4 groups and we are interested in one of these groups. $\frac{4}{1}$ means that the whole set is one group and we are interested in 4 of these groups which is the same as 4 whole sets.

3. **A.** $4 \times 3 = 12$ apples

   B. *$4 \times 6 = 24$ apples

   C. Multiplication

4. **A.** $\frac{1}{4} \times 24 = 6$ apples

   B. $\frac{2}{4} \times 24 = 12$ apples

   C. $\frac{3}{4} \times 24 = 18$ apples

   D. $\frac{4}{4} \times 24 = 24$ apples

5. **A.** All of the number sentences show the multiplication of a fraction times 24. The fraction increases by $\frac{1}{4}$ each time. The product increases by 6. You can get the products by skip counting by 6.

   B. 1; $1 \times 24 = 24$ apples

6.*

Multiplication Number Sentences
$\frac{1}{3} \times 12 = 4$
$\frac{2}{3} \times 12 = 8$
$\frac{3}{3} \times 12 = 12$
$\frac{4}{3} \times 12 = 16$
$\frac{5}{3} \times 12 = 20$
$\frac{6}{3} \times 12 = 24$

7. **A.** *See possible answers in Lesson Guide 3. Multiplying 12 by a fraction less than one is the same as finding a fractional part of 12. So, the product will be less than 12.

   B. The product is less than 12 when the fraction is less than 1.

   C. *The product is equal to 12 when the fraction is $\frac{3}{3}$. $\frac{3}{3} = 1$ and multiplying a number by 1 gives the same number.

   D. The product is greater than 12 when the fraction is greater than 1. Multiplying a number by a fraction greater than one means that you have more than one group of 12, so the product will be greater than 12.

8. **A.** $\frac{1}{4} \times 12 = 3$

   B. $\frac{2}{4} \times 12 = 6$

   C. $\frac{3}{4} \times 12 = 9$

   D. $\frac{4}{4} \times 12 = 12$

*Answers and/or discussion are included in the Lesson Guide.

**Answers for all the Home Practice in the *Discovery Assignment Book* are at the end of the unit.

E.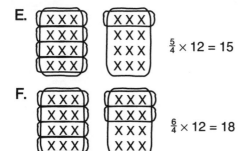

$\frac{5}{4} \times 12 = 15$

F.

$\frac{6}{4} \times 12 = 18$

Homework (SG pp. 385–386)

Questions 1–7

1. **A.** 6 apples

$\frac{1}{2} \times 12 = 6$ apples

B. 3 apples

$\frac{1}{4} \times 12 = 3$ apples

2. **A.** 4 apples

$\frac{1}{6} \times 24 = 4$ apples

B. 20 apples

$\frac{5}{6} \times 24 = 20$ apples

3. **A.** 8 apples

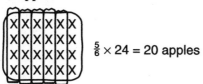

$\frac{1}{3} \times 24 = 8$ apples

B. 3 apples

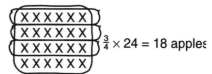

$\frac{1}{8} \times 24 = 3$ apples

C. 18 apples

$\frac{3}{4} \times 24 = 18$ apples

D. 20 apples

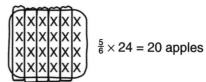

$\frac{5}{6} \times 24 = 20$ apples

4.

Multiplication Number Sentences
$\frac{1}{4} \times 8 = 2$
$\frac{2}{4} \times 8 = 4$
$\frac{3}{4} \times 8 = 6$
$\frac{4}{4} \times 8 = 8$
$\frac{5}{4} \times 8 = 10$
$\frac{6}{4} \times 8 = 12$

5. **A.** Answers will vary. As the fraction gets larger, the product gets larger. You can find products by skip counting by 2 because $\frac{1}{4} \times 8 = 2$.

B. The product is equal to the number of muffins in the whole package when the fraction is $\frac{4}{4}$. $\frac{4}{4} = 1$, and when a number is multiplied by 1 the product is the same number.

C. The product is less than the number of muffins in the whole package when the fraction is less than 1. When the number of muffins is multiplied by a fraction less than 1, you are finding a part of the whole package.

*Answers and/or discussion are included in the Lesson Guide.

**Answers for all the Home Practice in the *Discovery Assignment Book* are at the end of the unit.

    D. The product is more than the number of
       muffins in the whole package when the
       fraction is greater than 1. When the number is
       multiplied by a fraction greater than 1, the
       product is more than one whole package.

    E. $\frac{1}{2}$; $\frac{1}{2} \times 8 = 4$

6. 12 muffins

7. A. 2

    B. 4

    C. 5

    D. 10

    E. 12

    F. 15

    G. 18

    H. 30

*Answers and/or discussion are included in the Lesson Guide.
**Answers for all the Home Practice in the *Discovery Assignment Book* are at the end of the unit.

LESSON GUIDE

Multiplication of Fractions

Estimated Class Sessions: 1

Students use pattern blocks to explore multiplication of fractions. First they model multiplying a fraction times a whole number. Then, they model multiplying two fractions. Paper-and-pencil procedures are developed in Lesson 5.

Key Content

- Multiplying a fraction times a whole number using pattern blocks.
- Multiplying a fraction times a fraction using pattern blocks.
- Estimating products of fractions.

Daily Practice and Problems: Bit for Lesson 4

6. Division Facts (URG p. 13)

Find the number n that makes each sentence true.

A. $42 \div 7 = n$ B. $320 \div 4 = n$

C. $56 \div n = 7$ D. $28 \div n = 7$

E. $n \div 6 = 4$ F. $n \div 8 = 6$

DPP Task is on page 45. Suggestions for using the DPPs are on page 45.

Materials List

Print Materials for Students

	Math Facts and Daily Practice and Problems	Activity	Homework	Written Assessment
Student Books					
Student Guide		*Multiplication of Fractions* Pages 387–389	*Multiplication of Fractions* Homework Section Page 389	
Discovery Assignment Book		*Pattern Block Record Sheet* Pages 195–197		
Teacher Resources					
Facts Resource Guide ◉	DPP Item 12G			
Unit Resource Guide ◉	DPP Items G–H Page 13 ◉			DPP Item H *Adding Mixed Numbers* Page 13 ◉

◉ *available on Teacher Resource CD*

All Transparency Masters, Blackline Masters, and Assessment Blackline Masters in the Unit Resource Guide are on the Teacher Resource CD.

Supplies for Each Student Pair

1 set of pattern blocks (at least 2–3 yellow hexagons, 6 red trapezoids, 10 blue rhombuses, 10 green triangles, 6 brown trapezoids, and 12 purple triangles)

Materials for the Teacher

Transparencies of *Pattern Block Record Sheet* Activity Pages (Discovery Assignment Book) Pages 195–197, optional
overhead pattern blocks, optional

Developing the Activity

Part 1. Multiplication of Fractions and Whole Numbers

Begin the lesson by reading and discussing the Multiplication of Fractions and Whole Numbers section on the *Multiplication of Fractions* Activity Pages in the *Student Guide.* The first page shows several ways to represent the multiplication problem $\frac{1}{2} \times 4$. The first diagram uses arrays similar to those in Lesson 3. The second diagram shows two different ways to model $\frac{1}{2}$ of 4 using pattern blocks. (See Figures 10 and 11.) As you discuss the examples in the *Student Guide,* show the examples on the overhead projector using overhead pattern blocks. Remind students that $\frac{1}{2}$ of 4 can be interpreted as $\frac{1}{2} \times 4$.

$\frac{1}{2}$ of 4 = 2

Figure 10: *One way to show $\frac{1}{2} \times 4$ using pattern blocks*

$\frac{1}{2}$ of 4 = 2

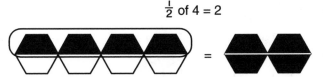

Figure 11: *Another way to show $\frac{1}{2} \times 4$ using pattern blocks*

One way to demonstrate the example in Figure 11 is to cover the top half of 4 yellow hexagons with 4 red trapezoids. Then, rearrange the 4 red trapezoids as shown to represent 2 wholes.

Finally, $\frac{1}{2} \times 4$ is compared to $4 \times \frac{1}{2}$. Students should remember that changing the order of the factors in a multiplication problem does not change the result. Ask students for examples of turnaround facts using whole numbers (e.g., 7×8 and 8×7 are turnaround facts). Pattern blocks are used to show $4 \times \frac{1}{2}$ as repeated addition as shown in Figure 12. So, $\frac{1}{2} \times 4 = 4 \times \frac{1}{2} = 2$.

Figure 12: $4 \times \frac{1}{2} = \frac{1}{2} + \frac{1}{2} + \frac{1}{2} + \frac{1}{2} = 2$

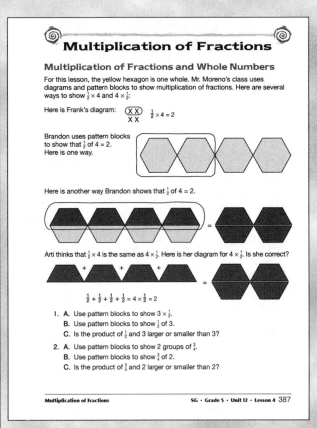

Student Guide - Page 387

Use **Questions 1–7** to lead a class discussion. Ask students to work in pairs to model the multiplication problems in the questions and report their results to the class. Figure 13 shows possible solutions to **Question 1.** To answer **Question 1A,** students can use repeated addition to show $3 \times \frac{1}{2}$ as $\frac{1}{2} + \frac{1}{2} + \frac{1}{2} = \frac{3}{2}$ or $1\frac{1}{2}$. To show $\frac{1}{2}$ of 3 in **Question 1B,** they start with three hexagons and then show that one-half of the 3 hexagons is $1\frac{1}{2}$ hexagons. Students should see that $\frac{1}{2}$ of 3 will be less than 3 since we are finding part of 3 **(Question 1C).**

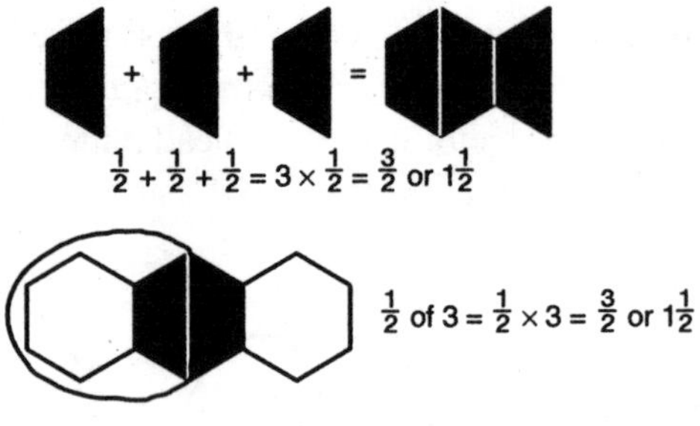

$$\frac{1}{2} + \frac{1}{2} + \frac{1}{2} = 3 \times \frac{1}{2} = \frac{3}{2} \text{ or } 1\frac{1}{2}$$

$$\frac{1}{2} \text{ of } 3 = \frac{1}{2} \times 3 = \frac{3}{2} \text{ or } 1\frac{1}{2}$$

Figure 13: $3 \times \frac{1}{2} = \frac{1}{2} \times 3 = \frac{3}{2}$ or $1\frac{1}{2}$

Questions 2A–2B ask students to show 2 groups of $\frac{3}{4}$ and to compare the result to $\frac{3}{4}$ of 2. When students are working on $\frac{3}{4}$ of 2, remind them to start with 2 yellow hexagons and then show $\frac{3}{4}$ of the 2 hexagons. (See Figure 14.)

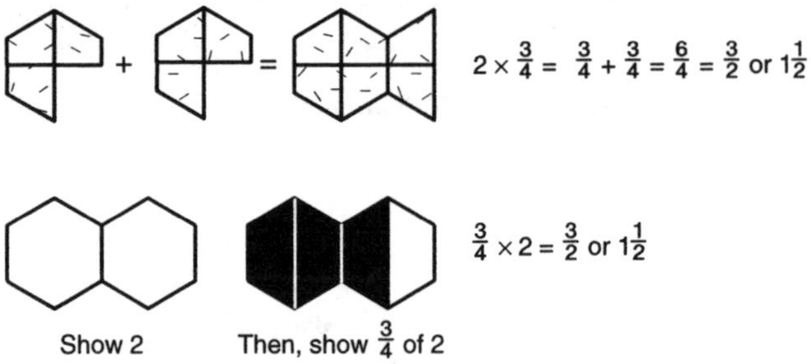

$$2 \times \frac{3}{4} = \frac{3}{4} + \frac{3}{4} = \frac{6}{4} = \frac{3}{2} \text{ or } 1\frac{1}{2}$$

$$\frac{3}{4} \times 2 = \frac{3}{2} \text{ or } 1\frac{1}{2}$$

Show 2   Then, show $\frac{3}{4}$ of 2

Figure 14: $2 \times \frac{3}{4} = \frac{3}{4} \times 2 = \frac{6}{4} = \frac{3}{2}$

Question 2C asks students to look back at their answers and decide if the product is more or less than 2. Encourage students to think about the size of the product. Finding $\frac{3}{4}$ of 2 means finding a part of 2, so the product will be smaller than 2. At the same time we know that the answer will be greater than $\frac{3}{4}$ because twice $\frac{3}{4}$ $(\frac{3}{4} + \frac{3}{4})$ will be greater than $\frac{3}{4}$.

Part 2. Multiplication of Two Fractions

The second part of the lesson extends the use of pattern blocks to modeling the multiplication of a fraction times a fraction. To show $\frac{2}{3} \times \frac{1}{2}$ using pattern blocks, first show $\frac{1}{2}$. Then, find $\frac{2}{3}$ of $\frac{1}{2}$. One-half of a whole (a yellow hexagon) is a red trapezoid. Two-thirds of a red trapezoid can be shown as two green triangles ($\frac{2}{6}$ of a yellow hexagon) or as one blue rhombus ($\frac{1}{3}$ of a yellow hexagon). (See Figure 15.)

Show $\frac{1}{2}$ Show $\frac{2}{3}$ of $\frac{1}{2}$

$$\frac{2}{3} \times \frac{1}{2} = \frac{2}{6} = \frac{1}{3}$$

Figure 15: $\frac{2}{3} \times \frac{1}{2} = \frac{2}{6} = \frac{1}{3}$

Question 4 asks students to consider the size of the product. The product of $\frac{2}{3} \times \frac{1}{2}$ is $\frac{1}{3}$. One-third is less than $\frac{1}{2}$ and also less than $\frac{2}{3}$ since we are finding a part of a fraction. Encourage students to think about the equivalent problem $\frac{1}{2}$ of $\frac{2}{3}$. One-half of two of anything is one of those things, so $\frac{1}{2}$ of $\frac{2}{3}$ is $\frac{1}{3}$.

Question 5 is similar to the example. Use pattern blocks on the overhead to help students get started. To show $\frac{1}{6}$ of $\frac{1}{2}$, begin with a red trapezoid to show $\frac{1}{2}$. Then, ask how they can show $\frac{1}{6}$ of $\frac{1}{2}$. Since 6 purple triangles fit on a red trapezoid, one purple triangle, or $\frac{1}{12}$ of a whole hexagon, is $\frac{1}{6}$ of $\frac{1}{2}$. (See Figure 16.) You may need to emphasize that the product of $\frac{1}{6} \times \frac{1}{2}$ is $\frac{1}{12}$ of the whole. Encourage students to look back at the result. The answer is less than $\frac{1}{2}$ because we are finding a part of $\frac{1}{2}$. Since we know that $\frac{1}{6} \times \frac{1}{2} = \frac{1}{2} \times \frac{1}{6}$, the answer will also be less than $\frac{1}{6}$ because we are finding a part of $\frac{1}{6}$.

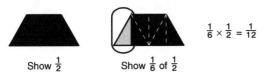

Show $\frac{1}{2}$ Show $\frac{1}{6}$ of $\frac{1}{2}$

$$\frac{1}{6} \times \frac{1}{2} = \frac{1}{12}$$

Figure 16: $\frac{1}{6} \times \frac{1}{2} = \frac{1}{12}$

---

3. Write number sentences for the following problems.
   A. Use pattern blocks to show $7 \times \frac{1}{6}$.
   B. Use pattern blocks to show $\frac{2}{3} \times 4$.

Multiplication of Two Fractions

Here is how Nicholas showed $\frac{2}{3} \times \frac{1}{2}$: First he showed $\frac{1}{2}$. Then he showed $\frac{2}{3}$ of $\frac{1}{2}$ by covering $\frac{2}{3}$ of a red trapezoid with green triangles.

$$\frac{2}{3} \times \frac{1}{2} = \frac{2}{6} \text{ or } \frac{1}{3}$$

Show $\frac{1}{2}$.   Then, show $\frac{2}{3}$ of $\frac{1}{2}$.

Then, he recorded his work on a *Pattern Block Record Sheet.*

$$\frac{2}{3} \times \frac{1}{2} = \frac{1}{3}$$

Using pattern blocks, he saw that $\frac{2}{3}$ of $\frac{1}{2}$ is $\frac{1}{3}$ of the whole.

Discuss

4. A. Is the product of $\frac{2}{3}$ and $\frac{1}{2}$ greater than or less than $\frac{1}{2}$?
   B. Is the product of $\frac{2}{3}$ and $\frac{1}{2}$ greater than or less than $\frac{2}{3}$?

5. A. Use pattern blocks to show $\frac{1}{6}$ of $\frac{1}{2}$.
   B. Is the product more or less than $\frac{1}{6}$?
   C. Is the product more or less than $\frac{1}{2}$?

6. A. Use pattern blocks to show $\frac{2}{3} \times \frac{3}{4}$.
   B. Is the product more or less than $\frac{2}{3}$?
   C. Is the product more or less than $\frac{3}{4}$?

388 **SG** · Grade 5 · Unit 12 · Lesson 4   **Multiplication of Fractions**

Student Guide - Page 388

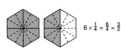

7. Use pattern blocks to show each of the following products.
   - First, estimate the size of the product.
   - Solve the problem and write a number sentence.
   - Reduce fractions to lowest terms, but do not change improper fractions to mixed numbers.
   - Record your work on a *Pattern Block Record Sheet*.

   A. $3 \times \frac{1}{12}$ B. $\frac{1}{3} \times \frac{1}{4}$ C. $\frac{5}{6} \times \frac{1}{2}$ D. $8 \times \frac{1}{6}$

Homework

Use the *Pattern Block Record Sheet* Activity Pages to show each of the following products.

   - First, estimate the size of the product.
   - Solve the problem and write a number sentence.
   - Reduce answers to lowest terms, but do not change improper fractions to mixed numbers.
   - Record your work on a *Pattern Block Record Sheet*.

   Follow the example: $6 \times \frac{1}{4}$

   $6 \times \frac{1}{4} = \frac{6}{4} = \frac{3}{2}$

   1. $3 \times \frac{1}{4} =$ 2. $10 \times \frac{1}{6} =$
   3. $2 \times \frac{1}{12} =$ 4. $4 \times \frac{1}{12} =$
   5. $2 \times \frac{5}{12} =$ 6. $\frac{1}{2} \times \frac{1}{2} =$
   7. $\frac{1}{3} \times \frac{3}{4} =$ 8. $\frac{2}{3} \times \frac{1}{4} =$
   9. $\frac{1}{2} \times \frac{1}{3} =$

Student Guide - Page 389

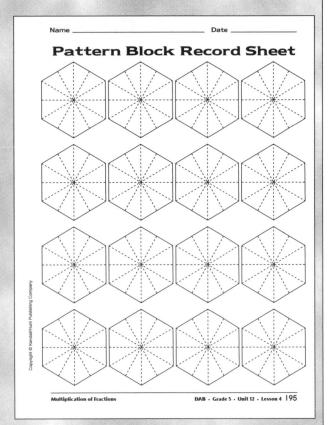

Name _____   Date _____

Pattern Block Record Sheet

Discovery Assignment Book - Page 195

One strategy for solving **Question 6** is shown in Figure 17. As students work, they may notice that it is possible to multiply numerators and denominators to find the product before giving the answer in lowest terms. Lesson 5 is designed to develop this procedure. At this time, encourage them to work more problems using pattern blocks to see if the procedure works with other problems.

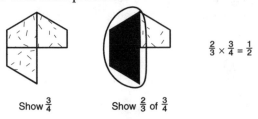

Show $\frac{3}{4}$ Show $\frac{2}{3}$ of $\frac{3}{4}$

$\frac{2}{3} \times \frac{3}{4} = \frac{1}{2}$

Figure 17: $\frac{2}{3} \times \frac{3}{4} = \frac{6}{12} = \frac{1}{2}$

Question 7 prepares students for the homework assignment. They must first estimate a product, solve the problem, write a number sentence, and then record their work on a *Pattern Block Record Sheet* Activity Page from the *Discovery Assignment Book*. For example, the problem in **Question 7B** is $\frac{1}{3} \times \frac{1}{4}$. Students can first estimate that the answer will be less than $\frac{1}{4}$, model the problem with pattern blocks, then record the solution on a *Pattern Block Record Sheet*. To estimate the answer to $8 \times \frac{1}{6}$ **(Question 7D)**, we can say that since $\frac{6}{6}$ is equal to 1, $8 \times \frac{1}{6}$ will be greater than 1. The solutions to **Questions 7A–7D** are shown in Figure 18.

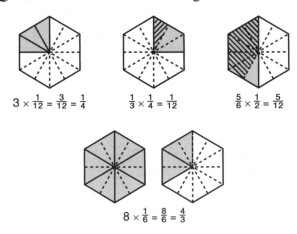

$3 \times \frac{1}{12} = \frac{3}{12} = \frac{1}{4}$ $\frac{1}{3} \times \frac{1}{4} = \frac{1}{12}$ $\frac{5}{6} \times \frac{1}{2} = \frac{5}{12}$

$8 \times \frac{1}{6} = \frac{8}{6} = \frac{4}{3}$

Figure 18: *Recording solutions on a Pattern Block Record Sheet*

Suggestions for Teaching the Lesson

Math Facts

DPP Bit G reviews the last six division facts using variables.

Homework and Practice

Assign the Homework section in the *Student Guide,* which is similar to Discussion *Question 7.* Students will need the *Pattern Block Record Sheet* Activity Pages from the *Discovery Assignment Book* to record their work.

Assessment

*   Check the homework problems for students' abilities to represent the solutions to the problems using pattern blocks and number sentences.
*   Use DPP Task H to assess students' abilities to add mixed numbers and write sums in lowest terms.

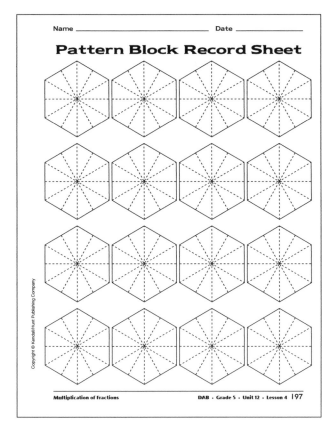

Discovery Assignment Book - Page 197

Daily Practice and Problems: Task for Lesson 4

H. Task: Adding Mixed Numbers
   (URG p. 13)

Use paper and pencil to solve the following problems. Write all fractions in lowest terms. Estimate to see if your answers are reasonable.

A. $8\frac{7}{10} + 2\frac{1}{10} =$

B. $2\frac{5}{9} + 3\frac{1}{3} =$

C. $3\frac{1}{12} + 4\frac{3}{8} =$

D. $5\frac{5}{6} + 2\frac{1}{2} =$

E. $5\frac{7}{10} + 2\frac{3}{5} =$

AT A GLANCE

Math Facts and Daily Practice and Problems

DPP Bit G reviews the last six facts. Task H includes problems in adding mixed numbers.

Part 1. Multiplication of Fractions and Whole Numbers

1. Students read and study the examples in the *Student Guide.* Model the examples on the overhead using overhead pattern blocks.
2. Use *Questions 1–3* to lead a class discussion in which students model multiplying a fraction times a whole number using pattern blocks.

Part 2. Multiplication of Two Fractions

1. Continue the class discussion using *Questions 4–6.* Students use pattern blocks to find the product of two fractions.
2. To answer *Question 7,* students estimate the size of the product, find the product of two fractions using pattern blocks, write a number sentence, then record their work on a *Pattern Block Record Sheet* from the *Discovery Assignment Book.*

Homework

Assign the Homework section in the *Student Guide.*

Assessment

1. Use DPP Task H as a quiz to assess students' abilities to add mixed numbers.
2. Check students' homework for their abilities to represent fractions using pattern blocks and number sentences.

Notes:

Student Guide

Questions 1–7 (SG pp. 387–389)

1. **A–B.** *See Figure 13 in Lesson Guide 4.

   C. *The product of $\frac{1}{2}$ and 3 is less than 3 since we are finding a part of 3.

2. **A–B.** *See Figure 14 in Lesson Guide 4.

   C. *The product of $\frac{3}{4}$ and 2 is smaller than 2 since we are finding a part of 2.

3. **A.**

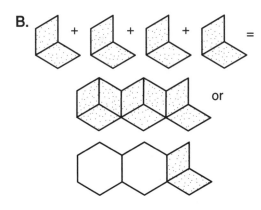

$$\frac{1}{6} + \frac{1}{6} + \frac{1}{6} + \frac{1}{6} + \frac{1}{6} + \frac{1}{6} + \frac{1}{6} = 7 \times \frac{1}{6} = \frac{7}{6} \text{ or } 1\frac{1}{6}$$

   B.

$$\frac{2}{3} + \frac{2}{3} + \frac{2}{3} + \frac{2}{3} = \frac{2}{3} \times 4 = \frac{8}{3} \text{ or } 2\frac{2}{3}$$

4. **A.** *Less than $\frac{1}{2}$

   B. *Less than $\frac{2}{3}$

5. **A.** *See Figure 16 in Lesson Guide 4.

   B. *Less than $\frac{1}{6}$

   C. *Less than $\frac{1}{2}$

6. **A.** *See Figure 17 in Lesson Guide 4.

   B. Less than $\frac{2}{3}$

   C. Less than $\frac{3}{4}$

7. **A.** *We can estimate the answer to be larger than $\frac{1}{12}$. See Figure 18 in Lesson Guide 4.

   B. *We can estimate the answer to be less than $\frac{1}{4}$. See Figure 18 in Lesson Guide 4.

   C. *We can estimate the answer to be less than $\frac{1}{2}$. See Figure 18 in Lesson Guide 4.

   D. *We can estimate the answer to be greater than 1 and less than 8. See Figure 18 in Lesson Guide 4.

Homework (SG p. 389)

Questions 1–9

1. We can estimate the answer to be more than $\frac{1}{4}$.

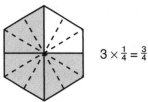

$$3 \times \frac{1}{4} = \frac{3}{4}$$

2. We can estimate the answer to be more than 1.

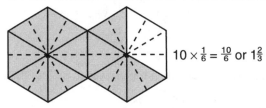

$$10 \times \frac{1}{6} = \frac{10}{6} \text{ or } 1\frac{2}{3}$$

3. We can estimate the answer to be greater than $\frac{1}{12}$.

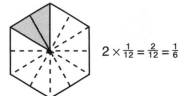

$$2 \times \frac{1}{12} = \frac{2}{12} = \frac{1}{6}$$

4. We can estimate the answer to be more than $\frac{1}{12}$.

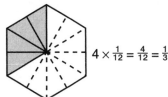

$$4 \times \frac{1}{12} = \frac{4}{12} = \frac{1}{3}$$

5. We can estimate the answer to be more than $\frac{1}{12}$ and less than 2.

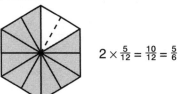

$$2 \times \frac{5}{12} = \frac{10}{12} = \frac{5}{6}$$

6. We can estimate the answer to be less than $\frac{1}{2}$.

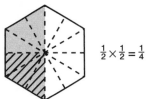

$$\frac{1}{2} \times \frac{1}{2} = \frac{1}{4}$$

*Answers and/or discussion are included in the Lesson Guide.

**Answers for all the Home Practice in the *Discovery Assignment Book* are at the end of the unit.

7. We can estimate the answer to be less than $\frac{1}{3}$.

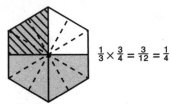

$\frac{1}{3} \times \frac{3}{4} = \frac{3}{12} = \frac{1}{4}$

8. We can estimate the answer to be less than $\frac{1}{4}$.

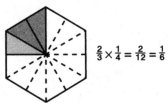

$\frac{2}{3} \times \frac{1}{4} = \frac{2}{12} = \frac{1}{6}$

9. We can estimate the answer to be less than $\frac{1}{3}$.

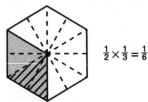

$\frac{1}{2} \times \frac{1}{3} = \frac{1}{6}$

*Answers and/or discussion are included in the Lesson Guide.
**Answers for all the Home Practice in the *Discovery Assignment Book* are at the end of the unit.

LESSON GUIDE 5

Using Patterns to Multiply Fractions

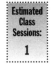
Estimated Class Sessions: 1

Part 1 of this lesson is a teacher-led activity. Students use paper folding to find the product of two fractions. They record their results and look for patterns that will help them generalize a procedure for multiplying fractions.

In Part 2, *Student Guide* pages review the paper-folding activity. Students practice multiplying fractions with paper and pencil. They also discuss strategies for estimating products of fractions so they can decide if their answers are reasonable.

Key Content

- Multiplying fractions using paper folding.
- Multiplying fractions using paper and pencil.
- Estimating products of fractions.
- Solving problems in more than one way.

Daily Practice and Problems: Bit for Lesson 5

I. More Division Fact Practice
(URG p. 13)

Find the number *n* that makes each sentence true.

A. $56 \div n = 8$

B. $480 \div n = 60$

C. $n \times 400 = 24,000$

D. $80 \times n = 3200$

E. $60 \times n = 420$

F. $n \div 7 = 400$

DPP Task is on page 54. Suggestions for using the DPPs are on page 54.

Materials List

Print Materials for Students

	Math Facts and Daily Practice and Problems	Activity	Homework
Student Books			
Student Guide		*Using Patterns to Multiply Fractions* Pages 390–391	*Using Patterns to Multiply Fractions* Homework Section Page 391
Discovery Assignment Book			Home Practice Parts 3 & 4 Page 190
Teacher Resources			
Facts Resource Guide	DPP Item 12I		
Unit Resource Guide	DPP Items I–J Pages 13–14		

available on Teacher Resource CD

All Transparency Masters, Blackline Masters, and Assessment Blackline Masters in the Unit Resource Guide are on the Teacher Resource CD.

Supplies for Each Student

scrap paper, several $8\frac{1}{2}$-inch by 11-inch sheets
crayons or colored pencils

Developing the Activity

Part 1. Using Paper Folding to Multiply Fractions

To begin this activity, briefly review the homework from the previous lesson. Discuss **Question 9** ($\frac{1}{2} \times \frac{1}{3}$). Compare the results from using the *Pattern Block Record Sheet* in the homework to the results from using paper folding in this lesson.

In this part of the activity, students will use paper folding to find the following products:

$$\frac{1}{2} \times \frac{1}{3}$$

$$\frac{3}{4} \times \frac{1}{2}$$

$$\frac{1}{2} \times \frac{3}{8}$$

$$\frac{5}{8} \times \frac{2}{3}$$

$$\frac{3}{4} \times \frac{2}{3}$$

When students have found the answers, they will write complete number sentences for each problem and look for patterns in the number sentences that will help them generalize a procedure for multiplying fractions. In order to be able to see the patterns, do **not** reduce the answers to lowest terms during this part of the lesson.

Before students read the *Student Guide* pages for this lesson, show them how to find the product of two fractions using paper folding as shown in Figure 19. To multiply $\frac{1}{2} \times \frac{1}{3}$, follow these steps:

- *Fold a scrap sheet of paper in thirds lengthwise.*
- *Unfold the paper, trace the folds, and color $\frac{1}{3}$ using one color crayon.*
- *Fold the paper in half horizontally.*
- *Unfold the paper, trace the fold, and color $\frac{1}{2}$ of the $\frac{1}{3}$ section using a different color.*
- *The fraction that is colored with both colors is $\frac{1}{2}$ of $\frac{1}{3}$.*

When students have completed the paper folding, ask:

- *How many parts is the paper divided into?* (6)
- *How many parts are shaded with both colors?* (1)
- *What fraction of the whole sheet of paper is $\frac{1}{2}$ of $\frac{1}{3}$?* ($\frac{1}{6}$)
- *Write a number sentence on your paper which shows the product of $\frac{1}{2}$ and $\frac{1}{3}$.* ($\frac{1}{2} \times \frac{1}{3} = \frac{1}{6}$. Write the number sentence on the board.)
- *Is $\frac{1}{2}$ of $\frac{1}{3}$ more or less than $\frac{1}{3}$? Why?* (Less. Because you are finding a part of $\frac{1}{3}$.)

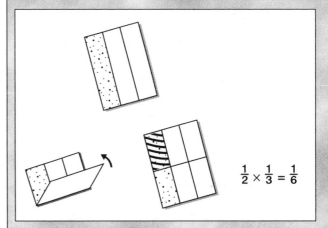

Figure 19: *Using paper folding to find the product of $\frac{1}{2} \times \frac{1}{3}$*

TIMS Tip

Remind students to crease the paper well with each fold. This will make it easier to outline the parts when the paper is unfolded.

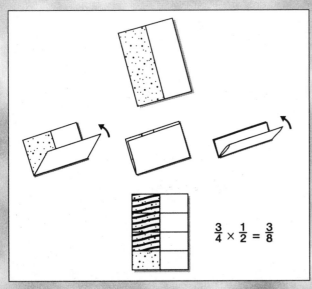

Figure 20: *Using paper folding to find the product of $\frac{3}{4} \times \frac{1}{2}$*

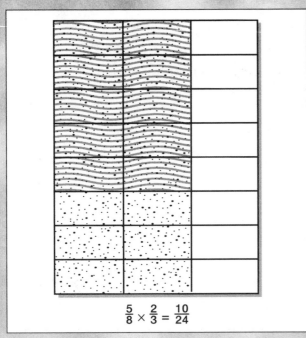

$$\frac{5}{8} \times \frac{2}{3} = \frac{10}{24}$$

Figure 21: *Using paper folding to find the product of $\frac{5}{8} \times \frac{2}{3}$*

Continue the lesson by using paper folding to find $\frac{3}{4}$ of $\frac{1}{2}$. (See Figure 20.) Students begin by folding a scrap sheet of paper in half lengthwise, unfolding the paper, tracing the fold, then coloring $\frac{1}{2}$. They fold the paper into fourths horizontally by folding the paper in half, then in half again. They then trace the folds and color $\frac{3}{4}$ of the colored section with a different color. Ask questions about this problem similar to the five questions above. Write $\frac{3}{4} \times \frac{1}{2} = \frac{3}{8}$ on the board under the first number sentence. It is important to encourage students to ask themselves if the answer is reasonable. They should see that the answer should be less than $\frac{1}{2}$ since multiplying by $\frac{3}{4}$ is finding a part of $\frac{1}{2}$.

Use a similar process to find $\frac{1}{2} \times \frac{3}{8}$, and $\frac{5}{8} \times \frac{2}{3}$, writing the results on the board in number sentences and discussing the number of parts in the whole and the number of parts that are shaded with two colors. Since $\frac{5}{8} \times \frac{2}{3}$ may be difficult for students, sample directions are given below (see Figure 21):

- *Fold a scrap sheet of paper into thirds lengthwise.*
- *Unfold the paper, trace the folds, and color $\frac{2}{3}$.*
- *Fold the paper into eighths horizontally by folding it in half (2 parts), then in half again (4 parts), and then in half one more time (8 parts).*
- *Unfold the paper, trace the folds, and color $\frac{5}{8}$ of the $\frac{2}{3}$ section using a different color.*
- *Count the total number of parts shown on the paper and count the number of parts that have been colored twice.*
- *Write a number sentence for the product of $\frac{5}{8}$ and $\frac{2}{3}$. Do not reduce the answer to lowest terms. ($\frac{5}{8} \times \frac{2}{3} = \frac{10}{24}$)*

Finally, find $\frac{3}{4} \times \frac{2}{3}$ in the same way and write the results in a number sentence without reducing the answer to lowest terms. When the class has found all the products, ask them to look for patterns in the five number sentences:

$$\frac{1}{2} \times \frac{1}{3} = \frac{1}{6}$$

$$\frac{3}{4} \times \frac{1}{2} = \frac{3}{8}$$

$$\frac{1}{2} \times \frac{3}{8} = \frac{3}{16}$$

$$\frac{5}{8} \times \frac{2}{3} = \frac{10}{24}$$

$$\frac{3}{4} \times \frac{2}{3} = \frac{6}{12}$$

Students may be able to see that to multiply fractions, we can multiply numerators and denominators as shown here:

$$\frac{3}{4} \times \frac{2}{3} = \frac{3 \times 2}{4 \times 3} = \frac{6}{12}$$

Part 2. Using Patterns to Multiply Fractions Using Paper and Pencil

The solution and strategy for solving $\frac{3}{4} \times \frac{2}{3}$ is discussed in detail in the *Using Patterns to Multiply Fractions* Activity Pages in the *Student Guide*. On those pages, a student explains that to show the multiplication, the paper is divided into 4×3 or 12 parts. 3×2 or 6 of those parts are colored twice. The discussion connects the paper folding with a paper-and-pencil procedure for multiplying fractions. As you begin work with paper-and-pencil procedures, be sure to remind students to check for the reasonableness of their answers.

Question 1A asks students to use the pattern to find the product of $\frac{2}{5}$ and $\frac{3}{4}$ and to reduce the answer to lowest terms. In *Question 1B,* they must decide if the answer is reasonable. The product $\frac{3}{10}$ is a reasonable answer since it is less than $\frac{3}{4}$. Finding a part of $\frac{3}{4}$ should result in a fraction smaller than $\frac{3}{4}$.

Question 2 challenges students to think about multiplication of fractions in more than one way. Two students solve the same problem. One uses standard paper-and-pencil procedures, and the other uses reasoning to solve the problem. Both methods produce a correct answer, although the first student did not give the answer in lowest terms.

Question 3 extends the pattern to the multiplication of a fraction and a whole number ($\frac{3}{5} \times 2$). Students are reminded that 2 can be written as $\frac{2}{1}$, so $\frac{3}{5} \times 2 = \frac{3}{5} \times \frac{2}{1} = \frac{3 \times 2}{5 \times 1} = \frac{6}{5}$.

Question 3C asks students to solve the problem another way. For example, $\frac{3}{5} \times 2$ can also be written as $\frac{3}{5} + \frac{3}{5} = \frac{6}{5}$.

Question 4 provides some practice before students are asked to solve similar problems on their own. As the class discusses the solutions to the problems, encourage them to discuss strategies for determining the reasonableness of their answers. Also, through class discussion of student strategies, encourage students to think about other possible ways of solving the problems besides using the standard pencil-and-paper procedure. For example, for *Question 4B,* students may reason that since $\frac{1}{3}$ of 3 is 1, $\frac{1}{3}$ of $\frac{3}{10}$ is $\frac{1}{10}$.

Journal Prompt
Find a way to solve $\frac{1}{4} \times \frac{4}{5}$ without multiplying the numerators and denominators. Describe your strategy.

Using Patterns to Multiply Fractions

Mr. Moreno's class used paper folding to investigate multiplication of fractions. After solving several problems this way, they looked for a pattern to help them multiply fractions with pencil and paper. Shannon explained her group's strategy using $\frac{3}{4} \times \frac{2}{3}$ as an example:

"To multiply $\frac{3}{4} \times \frac{2}{3}$, we folded a sheet of paper into thirds the long way, traced the folds, and colored $\frac{2}{3}$ yellow.

$\frac{2}{3}$

"Then we folded the paper into fourths the other way, traced the folds, and colored $\frac{3}{4}$ of the $\frac{2}{3}$ with blue.

"We saw that we had divided the paper into 4×3 or 12 parts, and we colored 3×2 or 6 of the 12 parts blue. So, $\frac{6}{12}$ of the parts are colored blue. That's the same as $\frac{1}{2}$, so we wrote:

$\frac{3}{4}$ of $\frac{2}{3}$

$$\frac{3}{4} \times \frac{2}{3} = \frac{3 \times 2}{4 \times 3} = \frac{6}{12} = \frac{1}{2}$$

"Our answer makes sense because we know that the answer should be less than $\frac{2}{3}$, since we were finding a part of $\frac{2}{3}$."

Discuss

1. A. Multiply $\frac{2}{5} \times \frac{3}{4}$ using paper and pencil. Reduce your answer to lowest terms.
   B. Is your answer reasonable? Why?

2. Felicia and Edward solved the problem $\frac{1}{2} \times \frac{4}{5}$ in two different ways. Felicia used paper and pencil and wrote the following:
   $$\frac{1}{2} \times \frac{4}{5} = \frac{1 \times 4}{2 \times 5} = \frac{4}{10}$$
   Edward reasoned that since $\frac{1}{2}$ of 4 is 2, then $\frac{1}{2}$ of $\frac{4}{5} = \frac{2}{5}$. Who is correct? Explain.

Student Guide - Page 390

---

3. Multiply $\frac{3}{5} \times 2$. (*Hint:* You can write 2 as $\frac{2}{1}$.)
   A. Should the answer be more or less than 2?
   B. Should the answer be more or less than 1?
   C. Solve the problem another way. Explain your strategy.
4. Solve. Reduce your answers to lowest terms. Is your answer reasonable?
   A. $\frac{2}{3} \times \frac{3}{5} =$ B. $\frac{1}{3} \times \frac{3}{10} =$ C. $\frac{3}{4} \times 6 =$ D. $\frac{2}{5} \times \frac{5}{8} =$

Homework

Find the following products. Write your answers in lowest terms.

1. $\frac{5}{8} \times \frac{1}{2} =$ 2. $\frac{1}{3} \times \frac{3}{8} =$ 3. $\frac{3}{10} \times \frac{1}{2} =$

4. $\frac{3}{8} \times \frac{3}{4} =$ 5. $\frac{3}{8} \times 4 =$ 6. $\frac{2}{3} \times \frac{2}{3} =$

7. $3 \times \frac{5}{6} =$ 8. $\frac{7}{10} \times \frac{1}{2} =$ 9. $10 \times \frac{4}{5} =$

10. $\frac{4}{5} \times \frac{3}{4} =$ 11. $8 \times \frac{2}{3} =$ 12. $\frac{2}{3} \times \frac{7}{8} =$

13. Brandon made a cheese pizza. He put pepperoni on $\frac{1}{2}$ of the pizza. He put onions on $\frac{3}{4}$ of the half with pepperoni. Draw a picture showing the toppings on the pizza.
    A. How much of the whole pizza has pepperoni and onions?
    B. How much of the whole pizza has only cheese?
    C. How much of the whole pizza has only pepperoni, but no onions?

14. A. Frank's guests ate $\frac{2}{3}$ of a cake at his party. How much cake was left over?
    B. The next day Frank ate $\frac{1}{4}$ of the leftover cake. How much of the whole cake did he eat the day after the party?

Student Guide - Page 391

Daily Practice and Problems: Task for Lesson 5

J. Task: Granola Bars (URG p. 14)

Lin's favorite granola bars come in packages of 10.

How many bars are in:

A. $\frac{1}{2}$ of a package?

B. $\frac{1}{10}$ of a package?

C. $\frac{3}{10}$ of a package?

D. $\frac{1}{5}$ of a package?

E. $\frac{3}{5}$ of a package?

F. $1\frac{1}{2}$ packages?

Suggestions for Teaching the Lesson

Math Facts

DPP item I reviews math facts in number sentences with unknown dividends, divisors, and factors.

Homework and Practice

- Assign the Homework section in the *Student Guide*.

- Assign DPP item J which reviews multiplying a whole number by a fraction.

- Assign some or all of the *Party Problems* in Lesson 7 for homework.

- Assign Parts 3 and 4 of the Home Practice which review fractions, percents, and computation.

Answers for Parts 3 and 4 of the Home Practice can be found in the Answer Key at the end of this lesson and at the end of this unit.

Assessment

Use *Questions 10–14* in the Homework section to assess students' abilities to multiply fractions.

Name _____   Date _____

Part 3 Fractions
Solve the following problems. Estimate to see if your answers are reasonable.

1. A. $\frac{1}{3} \times 15 =$ B. $\frac{1}{8} \times 24 =$ C. $\frac{2}{3} \times \frac{1}{6} =$

D. $\frac{1}{5} \times \frac{5}{6} =$ E. $\frac{1}{12} \times \frac{2}{5} =$ F. $\frac{3}{8} \times 16 =$

G. $\frac{1}{4}$ of $2.00 =$ H. $\frac{2}{5}$ of $50 =$ I. $\frac{3}{4}$ of $24 =$

2. Solve Question 1D a different way. Explain your strategy.

Part 4 Analyze the Class
In a class of 24 students:

1. 25% of the students are left-handed. How many students are left-handed?

2. $\frac{1}{3}$ of the class is wearing jeans. How many students are wearing jeans?

3. 18 students did extra credit math work. What fraction of the class did extra credit work?

4. What percent of the class did extra credit work?

5. 12 students are girls. What fraction of students are boys?

190 DAB · Grade 5 · Unit 12   USING FRACTIONS

Discovery Assignment Book - Page 190

AT A GLANCE

Math Facts and Daily Practice and Problems

DPP Bit I reviews math facts in number sentences with variables. Task J reviews multiplying whole numbers by fractions.

Part 1. Using Paper Folding to Multiply Fractions

1. Demonstrate to students how to find the product of $\frac{1}{2} \times \frac{1}{3}$ using paper folding.
2. Discuss the answer using the discussion prompts in the Lesson Guide. Then, write a number sentence for the problem.
3. Repeat the procedure for four more multiplication problems: $\frac{3}{4} \times \frac{1}{2}$, $\frac{1}{2} \times \frac{3}{8}$, $\frac{5}{8} \times \frac{2}{3}$, and $\frac{3}{4} \times \frac{2}{3}$. Solve each problem using paper folding, discuss the problem including the reasonableness of the results, and write a number sentence.
4. Look for patterns in the multiplication sentences and use the patterns to generalize a procedure for multiplying fractions using paper and pencil.

Part 2. Using Patterns to Multiply Fractions Using Paper and Pencil

1. Read and discuss the example on the *Using Patterns to Multiply Fractions* Activity Pages in the *Student Guide.*
2. Discuss *Questions 1–4* in the *Student Guide.* Encourage students to look for more than one way to solve the problems and always to check to see if their answers are reasonable.

Homework

1. Assign the Homework section in the *Student Guide.*
2. Assign Parts 3 and 4 of the Home Practice.
3. Use some or all of the *Party Problems* in Lesson 7 for homework.

Assessment

Use *Questions 10–14* in the Homework section as an assessment.

Notes:

Student Guide

Questions 1–4 (SG pp. 390–391)

1. **A.** $\frac{2}{5} \times \frac{3}{4} = \frac{2 \times 3}{5 \times 4} = \frac{6}{20} = \frac{3}{10}$

   B. *Yes; the answer should be less than $\frac{3}{4}$, since we are finding a part of $\frac{3}{4}$.

2. *Both students are right. If Felicia reduces her answer to lowest terms, she gets $\frac{2}{5}$ which is the same answer Edward wrote.

3. *$\frac{6}{5}$ or $1\frac{1}{5}$

   A. Less than 2, since we are finding a part of 2.

   B. More than 1. Since $\frac{3}{5}$ is greater than $\frac{1}{2}$, then $\frac{3}{5}$ of 2 should be more than $\frac{1}{2}$ of 2.

   C. *$\frac{3}{5} \times 2 = \frac{3}{5} + \frac{3}{5} = \frac{6}{5}$

4. **A.** $\frac{2}{5}$; the answer is reasonable since it should be less than $\frac{3}{5}$.

   B. *$\frac{1}{10}$; the answer is reasonable since it should be less than $\frac{3}{10}$.

   C. $\frac{9}{2}$ or $4\frac{1}{2}$; the answer is reasonable since it should be less than 6.

   D. $\frac{1}{4}$; the answer is reasonable since it should be less than $\frac{5}{8}$.

Homework (SG p. 391)

Questions 1–14

1. $\frac{5}{16}$

2. $\frac{1}{4}$

3. $\frac{3}{20}$

4. $\frac{9}{20}$

5. $\frac{3}{2}$ or $1\frac{1}{2}$

6. $\frac{4}{9}$

7. $\frac{5}{2}$ or $2\frac{1}{2}$

8. $\frac{7}{20}$

9. 8

10. $\frac{3}{5}$

11. $\frac{16}{3} = 5\frac{1}{3}$

12. $\frac{7}{12}$

13.

   A. $\frac{3}{8}$ **B.** $\frac{1}{2}$ **C.** $\frac{1}{8}$

14. **A.** $\frac{1}{3}$

   B. $\frac{1}{4} \times \frac{1}{3} = \frac{1}{12}$

Discovery Assignment Book

**Home Practice (DAB p. 190)

Part 3. Fractions

Questions 1–2

1. **A.** 5   **B.** 3

   C. $\frac{1}{9}$ **D.** $\frac{1}{6}$

   E. $\frac{1}{30}$ **F.** 6

   G. 50¢   **H.** $20

   I. $18

2. Two possible strategies:

   $\frac{1}{5} \times \frac{5}{6} = \frac{5}{30} = \frac{1}{6}$; $\frac{1}{5}$ of 5 is 1, so $\frac{1}{5}$ of $\frac{5}{6}$ is $\frac{1}{6}$.

Part 4. Analyze the Class

Questions 1–5

1. 6   2. 8

3. $\frac{3}{4}$ 4. 75%

5. $\frac{1}{2}$

*Answers and/or discussion are included in the Lesson Guide.

**Answers for all the Home Practice in the *Discovery Assignment Book* are at the end of the unit.

LESSON GUIDE 6

Peanut Soup

Estimated Class Sessions: 1

George Washington Carver shows his students at Tuskegee Institute the many food and nonfood products that he has been able to derive from peanut products in his lab. He tells them that he promised to help local farmers find a market for their peanut crops, but that the local businessmen have not yet accepted the idea that peanuts will make a good investment.

Together, Carver and his students decide to demonstrate the versatility of peanuts in a dramatic way by inviting a group of businessmen to a luncheon of dishes that contain peanuts. As they test the recipes and prepare the meal, Carver's students use fractions to convert recipes to the needed size. They also use various types of reasoning to create a schedule for cooking the meal.

In spite of minor setbacks, the meal is a great success, and the businessmen agree to support the farmers.

Key Content

- Creating a time schedule.
- Connecting mathematics to science and social studies: Learning about George Washington Carver.

Daily Practice and Problems: Bit for Lesson 6

K. Division (URG p. 14)

Try to solve the following problems in your head. Write the quotients as mixed numbers. Fractions should be in lowest terms.

A. $30 \div 7 =$ B. $60 \div 8 =$

C. $47 \div 6 =$ D. $26 \div 6 =$

E. $51 \div 6 =$ F. $35 \div 4 =$

DPP Task is on page 64. Suggestions for using the DPPs are on page 64.

Key Vocabulary

economic potential   nitrogen fixation
goobers   ratio
legumes

Curriculum Sequence

Before This Unit

In Unit 4 Lesson 7 students were introduced to George Washington Carver in the Adventure Book *George Washington Carver: A Man of Measure.*

After This Unit

The context of increasing or decreasing the number of servings made from a recipe will be used to review ratios and introduce proportions in Unit 13 Lesson 1.

Developing the Activity

We suggest that students first read the Adventure Book through to enjoy and understand the story. Then, use the following prompts to lead a class discussion.

Content Note

Tuskegee Normal and Industrial Institute was founded in 1881 by Booker T. Washington as a school where African-American boys and girls could learn to use science in practical ways. Its students were of diverse ages and economic backgrounds; some lived at the school, and some lived nearby. In addition to their studies, the students worked at the school, farming the gardens, tending the animals, helping in the kitchens, or constructing new buildings. Today Tuskegee Institute and the Carver Foundation continue research in the natural sciences. The Tuskegee Archives contain records of black history since 1896.

Materials List

Print Materials for Students

	Math Facts and Daily Practice and Problems	Activity	Homework
Students Books			
Adventure Book		*Peanut Soup* Pages 77–92	
Discovery Assignment Book			Home Practice Parts 5 & 6 Page 191
Teacher Resources			
Facts Resource Guide ⊙	DPP Item 12K		
Unit Resource Guide	DPP Items K–L Page 14 ⊙		

⊙ *available on Teacher Resource CD*

All Transparency Masters, Blackline Masters, and Assessment Blackline Masters in the Unit Resource Guide are on the Teacher Resource CD.

Discussion Prompts

Page 79

- *What had Professor Carver been working on so hard in his lab?*

He had been developing products made from peanuts.

- *What kinds of products did Carver make from peanuts?*

Shoe polish, face cream, milk, shaving cream, linoleum, house paint

Peanut Soup

Carver pointed to his lab table, which was covered with vials, pans, and bottles. "Everything you see here—this shoe polish, this face cream, even this glass of milk—I made from peanuts. The possibilities are endless! There's shaving cream, house paint—and look at this! I think this would make excellent linoleum! I made it from peanut shells."

"You made all this from *goobers*?" asked Eugene. "All this stuff?"

Before Carver could answer, young Buford, the smallest of the group, asked, "Why did you want to make stuff out of goobers?"

Carver gestured toward the window and the farmland beyond. "Well, Buford, it's because I made a promise to the farmers around here, and they've been asking me when I'm going to keep it."

"A promise?" Louis asked.

AB · Grade 5 · Unit 12 · Lesson 6   79

Adventure Book - Page 79

Page 80

- *What are legumes, and how do they affect the soil?*
- *What was Carver's promise to the farmers? What did he do to try to keep it?*

Carver promised the farmers that they could make a profit selling peanuts. He experimented and found many new uses for the peanut.

Content Note

Legumes are a family of plants including peas, beans, soybeans, peanuts, and clover. Legumes play a very important role in the process of farming. Nodules on the roots of legumes contain special bacteria capable of transforming unusable atmospheric nitrogen into a form of nitrogen which is usable by living organisms. This process is called **nitrogen fixation.**

Peanut Soup

"That's right," explained Carver. "I've been telling the farmers to plant peanuts instead of growing cotton. Our work here at Tuskegee has shown that peanuts are good for the soil and the crops they grow now are ruining the soil. You see, cotton takes nitrogen from the soil, and nitrogen must be present for most plants to grow. Peanuts and other legumes like cowpeas and soybeans put nitrogen back into the soil by 'fixing' it so that the plants can use it."

While Carver spoke, Eugene and Buford studied the items on the lab table. "Is there anything good to eat here?" Buford asked. "Sure, Buford," replied a skeptical Eugene, "Why don't you take a bite of that linoleum and tell me what you think!"

Alberta reminded Carver that he hadn't yet explained what his promise to the farmers had been.

"I promised that they would be able to make a profit by selling their peanuts," Carver said. "I told them that there would be a good market for their crops. Trouble is, I was the only one who could imagine the value of the peanut. But now, I have found dozens of ways for peanuts to be used!"

"Wow, Professor," exclaimed Louis, "I can hardly believe you made all of these things from goobers! Could I try the shoe polish?"

80   AB · Grade 5 · Unit 12 · Lesson 6

Adventure Book - Page 80

Peanut Soup

"Yes—try anything you like. And let me know what you think."

"This face cream is wonderful!" said Alberta. "Now will you show the farmers how to make all these things?"

"I'm afraid it's not that simple, Alberta," Carver replied. "Farmers don't have the time or the equipment to make all these things for themselves. What the farmers need is for someone to buy their peanuts. They need businessmen to open factories to make peanut products. Unfortunately, the businessmen around here don't think very highly of our lowly goober. I could show these products to local businessmen, and they would listen politely, but they would probably still think that goobers are only good for hog feed and fertilizer. I wish there were some way I could get them to 'catch the vision' and see all the economic potential that is locked up in a little peanut."

Buford had been waiting for a chance to be heard. "But, Professor, I don't see anything to eat here! The thing I like best about goobers is eating them. Why, all the folks I know like to eat goobers—doesn't everybody?"

Eugene was doubtful. "I don't think so, Buford—I know Black folks eat goobers, but I've never seen any white folks eating them."

"Hey, Professor—this is giving me an idea!" exclaimed Louis. "Maybe if we show those businessmen just how good goobers are to eat, they might be more willing to invest their money."

"You know, Louis, that's not a bad idea. What exactly did you have in mind?"

Adventure Book - Page 81

Peanut Soup

Alberta interrupted. "Please, just read the recipe and fetch the right amount of flour!"

Eugene picked up an enormous metal bowl and headed for the pantry. "If you say so."

Alberta addressed two of her fellow students, "While Eugene's getting the flour, we can look for the right-size pans."

Eugene returned from the pantry with a huge bowl of flour. "Here you go, Alberta. This is the first batch—I figure I'll have to fetch about ten more bowls to have enough."

Alberta stared down at him. "What are you thinking? There is enough flour here for two banquets!"

"No, ma'am," Eugene replied. "That recipe says plain as day that we need 70 pounds of flour for the bread."

Alberta took up the recipe. "Let me see that."

She read the instructions. "Well, no wonder! This recipe makes enough bread to feed half the students at Tuskegee! We'll have to make much less than this recipe says to make."

Adventure Book - Page 83

Discussion Prompts

Page 81

- *Why did Carver want the businessmen to know the many uses of the peanut?*

So they would buy the farmers' peanut crops and open factories to make peanut products.

- *What was Louis's idea?*

To have a big dinner of their favorite peanut dishes for the businessmen in order to impress them.

Page 83

- *Why did Eugene get too much flour for Alberta?*

Because he followed a recipe exactly, without considering the number of people it would serve.

Discussion Prompts

Page 84

- *What is a ratio? Give an example from the story.*

A **ratio** is a comparison of quantities, often expressed as a fraction. The ratio involved here is the number of people served at the luncheon compared with the number of people served by Alberta's recipe ($\frac{12 \text{ people}}{240 \text{ people}}$).

Page 85

- *How would you find $\frac{1}{20}$ of 70 pounds of flour?*

Answers will vary.

Peanut Soup

"That's a good idea," joked Eugene. "Maybe if we cut it down far enough, those businessmen won't even notice the peanuts in it."

"Don't be silly, Eugene. The amount of peanuts—I mean the ratio—of peanuts to bread will stay the same."

"Ratio?" asked Eugene.

"Relax," replied Alberta. "A ratio is just a fraction. We can use fractions to solve our flour problem."

"How?"

"Let's follow the Professor's advice and start with what we know. Look at your bread recipe and tell me how many people it serves."

Eugene looked at the recipe. "This says, 'Feeds 240.' "

"But we'll only have 12 men at the luncheon," Alberta pointed out.

"Yeah—so the recipe you gave me is way too big."

"Right! So can you tell me how much flour you'll need for our bread?"

"Let's see . . ." Eugene thought. "I think I can. If we divide 240 people by 12 people, we get 20. This means the recipe makes 20 times more than we need. So we should divide each ingredient by 20."

"Good thinking, Eugene! You're right. You do know how to use ratios!"

Eugene was puzzled. "Ratios? When did I use a ratio?"

Alberta patiently wrote out the ratio she had in mind:

$$\frac{\text{people served at luncheon}}{\text{people served with recipe}} = \frac{12 \text{ people}}{240 \text{ people}}$$

Eugene easily saw what Alberta was trying to say. "So ratios are like fractions," he said. "But wait a minute! That's not the way I did it. I divided 240 by 12. What you have is just the opposite. You are dividing 12 by 240. In arithmetic we learned that we always divide the numerator by the denominator."

***Adventure Book* - Page 84**

Peanut Soup

"Go ahead and divide and see what you get," suggested Alberta.

Eugene scribbled on the paper and announced, "I get .05 for an answer."

"Good," said Alberta. "Can you write that as a fraction?"

"Sure," answered Eugene. ".05 = $\frac{5}{100}$, and if I reduce that I get $\frac{1}{20}$."

Alberta pounced upon his answer: "That's why you divided the flour by 20! You were calculating the amount you will need for $\frac{1}{20}$ of the original recipe."

"I get it!" Eugene wrote the following equation on the paper: $\frac{12}{240} = .05 = \frac{5}{100} = \frac{1}{20}$. "These are all different ways of saying the same thing."

"So," said Alberta. "We agree that we need to find one-twentieth of all these ingredients. First, take the flour. What's $\frac{1}{20}$ of 70 pounds?"

"Let's write it down," suggested Eugene, "so we can figure it out."

Alberta and Eugene sat down with a pencil and paper. "Seventy pounds divided by twenty is three and one-half pounds," Alberta said, "so we need three and one-half pounds of flour for the smaller recipe." She wrote: 70 pounds ÷ 20 = $3\frac{1}{2}$ pounds.

***Adventure Book* - Page 85**

Peanut Soup

"Should I go to the lab and find a scale to weigh the flour?" Eugene asked.

"There's no need—we can easily measure it in cups," Alberta said. "There are about four cups of flour in a pound, and we need three and one-half pounds, so how many cups is that?"

"Well, let me see . . . three and one-half is seven halves, and seven halves times four equals 28 halves, which equals . . .14! We need 14 cups of flour."

Alberta wrote: 4 cups × 3½ = 14 cups.

"Good," Alberta said. "Now let's figure out the rest of the ingredients."

Meanwhile, Carver checked up on Josephine. "How's the soup recipe coming?" he asked.

"Fine!" Josephine replied. "The recipe only makes enough for four people, but since we're cooking for 12, we have to triple everything. We're just measuring the flour now. I figure we need 12 tablespoons. Charles, hand me that tablespoon, will you?"

Carver raised his hand. "Hold on a minute, Josephine—it will take a long time to measure 12 tablespoons one at a time. Can you think of a faster way?"

"Well, we have larger measures, but I don't know how many tablespoons they hold," Josephine said.

"That should be easy to figure out," Carver answered. "Why don't you find out how many tablespoons it takes to fill this quarter-cup?"

"The quarter-cup holds exactly four tablespoons," Josephine said. "Now I can use it to measure the flour."

"Very good, Josephine. I'll check back again in a while to see how you're doing."

86   AB · Grade 5 · Unit 12 · Lesson 6

Adventure Book - Page 86

Peanut Soup

Louis added, "We also have to figure out whether to bake all the cookies at the same time or whether we'll need to do them in different batches."

"Good thinking," agreed Carver. "I have to use the oven for the mock chicken starting at noon, so we can only bake one tray of cookies at a time."

Buford figured out loud. "So if we make 3 cookies each for 12 people, that's 36 cookies, or three dozen. We can put a dozen cookies on a tray. That means we'll need three trays."

Louis was impressed. "Hey, that's really using your head, Buford! So I'll have to bake three trays of cookies, one tray at a time. If we allow 15 minutes to mix and shape the cookies and add an extra 15 minutes to be on the safe side, we should start the cookies at a quarter till twelve."

Louis was pleased with their planning. "Finally we have a schedule!"

11:45 Start making cookies.
12:00 Put mock chicken loaf in oven.
12:00 Begin creamed vegetable.

"This meal is shaping up very nicely," Carver declared. "I can't wait until Saturday to see the expressions on the faces of our guests when I tell them what they've been eating!"

"Well, I can wait!" Eugene said. "In fact, I think I'll just go wait in my room. Just let me know when it's all over."

88   AB · Grade 5 · Unit 12 · Lesson 6

Adventure Book - Page 88

Discussion Prompts

Page 86

- *If there are about 4 cups of flour in a pound, how many cups do you need for $3\frac{1}{2}$ pounds? How would you solve this problem?*

14 cups. Solutions will vary. Alberta changed $3\frac{1}{2}$ pounds to $\frac{7}{2}$ pounds and then multiplied $\frac{7}{2}$ by 4. Another strategy is to multiply $4 \times 3\frac{1}{2}$ by multiplying $4 \times 3 = 12$ and $4 \times \frac{1}{2} = 2$. Then, $12 + 2 = 14$ cups.

- *How many tablespoons are in a quarter-cup (one-fourth cup)?*

4 tablespoons

- *How many times will Josephine have to refill the quarter-cup to measure 12 tablespoons?*

3 times. She needs $\frac{3}{4}$ cup of flour.

Page 88

- *How did Louis decide to start making the cookies at a quarter till twelve?*

15 min (to mix and shape the cookies) + 45 min (to bake 3 trays at 15 min per tray) = 60 min or 1 hr

Louis added an extra 15 min "to be on the safe side," so they needed to start baking cookies 1 hr and 15 min before the luncheon or at 11:45.

Discussion Prompts

Page 91

- *Why did Carver want to have greens with the meal? Why did he want several different kinds?*

According to the story, a mix of greens tastes better than a single type of green by itself. Also, the greens provide nutritional balance.

Historical Note

George Washington Carver wrote bulletins about the medicinal and nutritional properties of wild plants and vegetables. During the first World War, his bulletins helped people locate, harvest, and prepare wild greens that were not only good to eat, but also good for them. One such green was the pokeweed as shown here.

Page 92

- *Were the guests surprised to learn that all the dishes contained peanuts? Was the luncheon a success?*

Yes. The businessmen enjoyed all the dishes and were amazed to find that there were peanuts in all the dishes. They agreed that peanuts might be profitable.

Content Note

Peanut Soup is based on more than one true incident in Carver's career in Tuskegee. To stage dramatic presentations of his work with the peanut, sweet potato, or cowpea, Carver delighted in serving meals made entirely with dishes containing these items. He waited until after the guests had finished their meal to tell them what they had eaten. He invariably took the opportunity to demonstrate other nonfood uses of the legume as well and won over many skeptics in this way.

Peanut Soup

Buford was quick to apologize for the trouble. "I sure am sorry, Professor—I was only trying to help. I'll do better now! I'll find the best greens, and I'll carry them for you, and I'll help you wash them and toss them—these will be the best darned greens those old high-hats ever ate! These greens—"

"Buford," interrupted Carver, stooping to pick some greens, "there's no need to be disrespectful toward our guests. Some of these 'high-hats,' as you call them, are good friends of mine, and many of them have done a lot to help Tuskegee."

"Yes, sir. I'm sorry. Hey, Professor—look at all these dandelion greens! There are enough here for ten luncheons."

"Yes, but wild greens taste best when you use a variety. I'd like to find some pokeweed and some rabbit tobacco. Let's look over there. . . ."

Meanwhile, the students were getting nervous in the kitchen. "I hope Professor Carver returns soon," said Eugene as he looked out the window. "I don't see him anywhere. Those greens might be the only good part of this meal!"

Alberta looked around the kitchen. "Everything's ready! All we need are the greens. But where can Professor Carver be?"

AB · Grade 5 · Unit 12 · Lesson 6   91

Adventure Book - Page 91

Peanut Soup

Eugene looked out the door. "I don't know. Maybe they decided to skip this nutty lunch!"

Just then, Carver and Buford returned with their arms full of greens. "Here we are! How's it going?"

"Thank goodness you're back!" Alberta cried. "You're just in time to greet the guests!"

Buford turned to Eugene. "Quick—help me wash these greens!"

The Tuskegee luncheon was a great success. After the meal, when the guests had eaten enthusiastically and praised the cooks, Carver announced that every dish had contained peanuts.

The businessmen were amazed and asked many questions. They learned that milk and butter—even pickles—could be made from the lowly goober, as well as cheese, coffee, and many useful nonfood products. Carver explained how the peanut was an easy crop to grow and how it enriched the soil. The businessmen agreed that there might be a profitable future for the peanut.

And Eugene scrubbed all the pots.

92   AB · Grade 5 · Unit 12 · Lesson 6

Adventure Book - Page 92

Daily Practice and Problems: Task for Lesson 6

L. Task: Multiplying Fractions N ※
  (URG p. 14)

Multiply these fractions. Reduce answers to lowest terms. Estimate to see if your answers are reasonable.

A. $\frac{1}{2} \times \frac{1}{4} =$ B. $\frac{1}{4} \times \frac{1}{4} =$

C. $\frac{2}{3} \times \frac{1}{2} =$ D. $\frac{3}{8} \times \frac{1}{6} =$

E. $\frac{5}{8} \times \frac{2}{3} =$ F. $\frac{1}{2} \times \frac{3}{5} =$

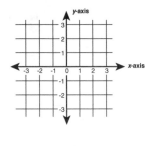

Name _____ Date _____

Part 5 Let's Practice
Use paper and pencil to solve the following. Use a separate sheet of paper to show your work.

A. $3\frac{4}{5} + 7\frac{1}{4} =$ B. $862 \times 9 =$ C. $94 \times 34 =$

D. $53.68 + 0.432 =$ E. $7341 \div 9 =$ F. $82 - 14.65 =$

Part 6 Working with Coordinates

I. A. Plot the coordinates in the table. Record the ordered pairs. Label the points with a letter on the graph.

Point	x-coordinate	y-coordinate	Ordered Pairs
A	-2	-1	
B	-3	-3	
C	-1	-3	
D	1	3	

B. You will need a ruler for this problem. If 1 cm ≡ 200 cm on the graph, what is the distance between A and D?

USING FRACTIONS   DAB · Grade 5 · Unit 12 191

Discovery Assignment Book - Page 191

Suggestions for Teaching the Lesson

Math Facts

DPP Bit K reviews math facts in division sentences with quotients as mixed numbers.

Homework and Practice

- Assign DPP Task L to practice multiplying fractions.
- Assign Parts 5 and 6 of the Home Practice which review operations with fractions and decimals and coordinate geometry.

Answers for Parts 5 and 6 of the Home Practice can be found in the Answer Key at the end of this lesson and at the end of this unit.

Extensions

- Ask students to take a favorite family recipe and expand it to serve 12 people.
- Students can make a menu for a special meal with their family and make a list of ingredients they will need and plan a schedule for preparing the meal.

Literature Connections

- Adair, Gene. *George Washington Carver: Botanist*. Chelsea House Publishers, New York, 1989.
- Carter, Andy, and Carol Saller. *George Washington Carver*. Carolrhoda Books, Inc., Minneapolis, MN, 2001.
- Mitchel, Barbara. *A Pocketful of Goobers*. Carolrhoda Books, Inc., Minneapolis, MN, 1989.
- Moore, Eva. *The Story of George Washington Carver*. Scholastic, New York, 1995.

Resources

- Carver, George W. "How to Grow the Peanut and 105 Ways of Preparing it for Human Consumption." *Bulletin No. 31*. Experiment Station, Tuskegee Normal and Industrial Institute, Tuskegee, AL, June 1925.
- Carver, George W. "Nature's Garden for Victory and Peace." *Bulletin No. 43*. Experiment Station, Tuskegee Normal and Industrial Institute, Tuskegee, AL, March 1942.
- Holt, Rackham. *George Washington Carver: An American Biography*. Doubleday, New York, 1961.
- Kremer, Gary R. *George Washington Carver: In His Own Words*. University of Missouri Press, Columbia, MO, 1987.
- McMurry, Linda L. *George Washington Carver: Scientist and Symbol*. Oxford University Press, New York, 1981.

Discovery Assignment Book

**Home Practice (DAB p. 191)

Part 5. Let's Practice

Questions A–F

A. $11\frac{1}{20}$ **B.** 7758

C. 3196   **D.** 54.112

E. 815 R6 or $815\frac{2}{3}$ **F.** 67.35

Part 6. Working with Coordinates

Question 1

I. **A.**

Point	x-coordinate	y-coordinate	Ordered Pair
A	-2	-1	(-2, -1)
B	-3	-3	(-3, -3)
C	-1	-3	(-1, -3)
D	1	3	(1, 3)

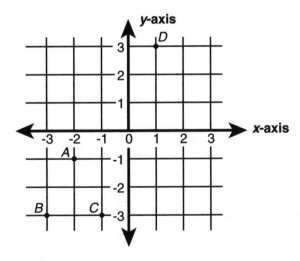

B. 1000 cm

*Answers and/or discussion are included in the Lesson Guide.

**Answers for all the Home Practice in the *Discovery Assignment Book* are at the end of the unit.

OPTIONAL LESSON

There are no Daily Practice and Problems items for this lesson.

LESSON GUIDE

Party Problems

Students solve a variety of multistep word problems.

Estimated Class Sessions: 1

Key Content

- Solving multistep word problems.
- Solving problems involving fractions.
- Communicating solutions orally and in writing.
- Choosing appropriate methods and tools to calculate (calculators, paper and pencil, or mental math).
- Choosing to find an estimate or an exact answer.

Materials List

Print Materials for Students

	Optional Activity
Student Guide	*Party Problems* Pages 392–393

Student Book

Supplies for Each Student

calculator

Developing the Activity

This problem set can serve many purposes. It can present opportunities to choose appropriate methods to solve problems. It can also be used to supplement homework for the unit or be used as an assessment.

Questions 1–6 cover concepts learned in this unit. *Questions 7–10* review concepts learned in previous units. You may choose to assign some or all of the problems to reinforce concepts in preparation for the midterm test in Lesson 8.

Student Guide - Page 392

Party Problems

Solve the following problems. Show how you solved each problem.

1. Jeff's sister made a HAPPY BIRTHDAY sign for Jeff. Since Jeff is 10 years old, his sister drew 10 flowers. She colored $\frac{2}{5}$ of the flowers yellow and the rest she colored red. What fraction of the flowers are red?

2. At the beginning of the party, Jeff set 18 cups of lemonade on the table. After the party was over, $\frac{1}{6}$ of the cups of lemonade were left. How many cups of lemonade did Jeff's guests drink?

3. Jeff's mother bought 2 bags of balloons. Each bag contained 8 balloons. She used $1\frac{1}{4}$ bags of balloons to decorate the room. How many balloons did she use?

4. For the party, Jeff's mother bought sandwich trays from the Servin' Sandwiches Shop. Each tray contained 9 sandwiches. The party guests left $\frac{2}{3}$ of a tray of sandwiches. How many sandwiches did they leave?

5. To make a pitcher of lemonade, Jeff needed 8 cups of water. He could only find a $\frac{1}{3}$-cup measuring cup. How many times did Jeff fill the $\frac{1}{3}$-cup when he made the lemonade?

6. One-half of Jeff's guests were relatives. Three-fifths of the relatives were cousins.
   A. What fraction of his guests were cousins?
   B. Jeff had 20 guests at his party. How many of the guests were cousins?

392 SG · Grade 5 · Unit 12 · Lesson 7   Party Problems

Student Guide - Page 393

7. Jeff's family spent $77.50 on the party. If there were 20 guests at the party, about how much money did they spend on each guest?

8. It was very cold when the guests arrived at the party. The temperature was -5°F. When the guests left, the temperature was -17°F. What was the difference between the two temperatures?

9. Jeff had a total of 43 favors to give to his guests. If each guest got the same number of favors, how many favors did each guest take home? How many favors were left over?

10. Jeff's mother created a riddle for the guests to solve:

   Today is also Jeff's uncle's birthday. His age has 2 and 5 as some of its factors. 3 is not a factor. His age is more than the square of 7 but less than the square of 8.
   A. Is Jeff's uncle's age prime or composite?
   B. What is the square of 7? of 8?
   C. What is Jeff's uncle's age?

Party Problems   SG · Grade 5 · Unit 12 · Lesson 7 393

Suggestions for Teaching the Lesson

Homework and Practice

Assign some or all of the questions for homework.

AT A GLANCE

Developing the Activity

Students complete *Questions 1–10* on the *Party Problems* Activity Pages in the *Student Guide*.

Homework

Assign some or all of the problems for homework.

Notes:

Student Guide

Questions 1–10 (SG pp. 392–393)

Solution strategies will vary for *Questions 1–10.*

1. $\frac{3}{5}$

2. 15 cups; There are $18 \times \frac{1}{6} = 3$ cups left. Therefore, the guests drank $18 - 3 = 15$ cups of lemonade.

3. 10 balloons. 1 bag has 8 balloons. $\frac{1}{4}$ bag has $\frac{1}{4} \times 8 = 2$ balloons. So, $1\frac{1}{4}$ bags have $8 + 2 = 10$ balloons.

4. 6 sandwiches; $9 \times \frac{2}{3} = 6$

5. 24 times

6. **A.** $\frac{3}{10}$ cousins; $\frac{3}{5} \times \frac{1}{2} = \frac{3}{10}$
   B. 6; $\frac{3}{10} \times 20 = 6$

7. Estimates will vary. One possible solution is $\$80 \div 20 = \$4$.

8. 12°F

9. Each guest got 2 favors with 3 favors left over. $43 \div 20 = 2$ R3.

10. **A.** Composite, since it has 2 and 5 as some of its factors.
    B. $7^2 = 49$ and $8^2 = 64$
    C. 50 years old. If a number has both 2 and 5 as factors, 10 is also a factor. The multiples of 10 between 49 and 64 are 50 and 60. Jeff's uncle's age is 50 since 3 is a factor of 60, but not of 50.

*Answers and/or discussion are included in the Lesson Guide.

**Answers for all the Home Practice in the *Discovery Assignment Book* are at the end of the unit.

LESSON GUIDE 8

Midterm Test

Students take a paper-and-pencil test consisting of 14 items. These items test skills and concepts studied in Units 9 through 12.

Key Content

- Assessing concepts and skills developed in Units 9 through 12.

Daily Practice and Problems: Bit for Lesson 8

M. Fact Practice (URG p. 15)

A. $60 \times 80 =$

B. $420 \div 70 =$

C. $32,000 \div 400 =$

D. $70 \times 8 =$

E. $2400 \div 6 =$

F. $7000 \times 40 =$

DPP Task is on page 70. Suggestions for using the DPPs are on page 70.

Materials List

Print Materials for Students

	Math Facts and Daily Practice and Problems	Homework	Written Assessment
Student Book — Discovery Assignment Book		Home Practice Part 7 Page 192	
Teacher Resources — Facts Resource Guide	DPP Item 12M		
Teacher Resources — Unit Resource Guide	DPP Items M–N Page 15		*Midterm Test* Pages 72–77, 1 per student

available on Teacher Resource CD

All Transparency Masters, Blackline Masters, and Assessment Blackline Masters in the Unit Resource Guide are on the Teacher Resource CD.

Supplies for Each Student

calculator
ruler
pattern blocks

Daily Practice and Problems:
Task for Lesson 8

N. Task: Inheriting Money
(URG p. 15)

Krista's uncle died and left her his money. In order to claim her fortune, she has to solve this riddle which tells the amount she inherited.

Take your time to find a prime.
But, beware, it's one more than a square.
It's under one hundred and ends in seven.
Now, add six zeros and you'll be in heaven.
Problems, you say, there's more than one solution?
Then, add them, my dear, and enjoy your fortune.

How much money did Krista inherit?

Part 7 Food for Thought

Solve the following problems. You may use any of the tools you have used in class such as calculators, drawings, or pattern blocks. Show your solutions.

1. A. If three friends split $1\frac{1}{2}$ pizzas evenly, how much of a whole pizza will each person eat?

    B. If six friends split $1\frac{1}{2}$ pizzas, how much of a whole pizza will each person eat?

2. Michael's father made a pumpkin pie. Michael and his brother couldn't wait until after dinner to eat the pie. Michael ate $\frac{1}{8}$ of the pie. His brother ate $\frac{1}{4}$ of the pie. What fraction of the whole pie was left for dessert after dinner?

3. Ana is making nut bread for a bake sale. The recipe for one loaf of bread calls for $\frac{3}{4}$ cup of nuts. If she wants to make 5 loaves of bread, how many cups of nuts does she need?

4. David is making orange punch. He combines $5\frac{1}{4}$ cups of orange juice with $2\frac{2}{3}$ cups of sparkling water. Can he pour all the punch into a 2-quart pitcher? Why or why not? (1 quart = 4 cups)

5. A muffin recipe calls for $\frac{1}{3}$ cup of blueberries for each pan of muffins. If Blanca picked 3 cups of berries, how many pans of muffins can Blanca make?

192 DAB · Grade 5 · Unit 12   USING FRACTIONS

Discovery Assignment Book - Page 192

Developing the Activity

Students take the test individually. Although the test is designed to take one class session for students to complete, you may wish to give them more time. Part 1 of the test consists of 2 division problems. These problems are included in the test to assess students' fluency with paper-and-pencil methods for division. Students should complete these items without the use of a calculator. Once students have completed these items, they should have calculators, rulers, and pattern blocks readily available for the remaining problems on the test in Part 2.

Ask students to follow the directions for each item. Some of the items ask students to tell how they solved the problem. Encourage them to give full explanations of the problem-solving process used.

Suggestions for Teaching the Lesson

Math Facts

DPP Bit M reviews the last six facts with multiples of ten.

Homework and Practice

• Assign DPP Task N which involves solving a riddle.

• Assign Home Practice Part 7.

Answers for Part 7 of the Home Practice can be found in the Answer Key at the end of this lesson and at the end of this unit.

Assessment

Add this test to students' portfolios so you can compare students' performance on this test to their performance on similar activities throughout the year.

AT A GLANCE

Math Facts and Daily Practice and Problems

DPP Bit M reviews the last six facts. Task N involves problem solving.

Developing the Activity

1. Students complete Part 1 of the *Midterm Test* without a calculator.
2. Students complete Part 2 of the test. Calculators, rulers, and pattern blocks should be made available.

Homework

1. Assign DPP Task N for homework.
2. Assign Part 7 of the Home Practice.

Assessment

Add this test to students' portfolios to compare to similar assessments.

Notes:

Midterm Test

Part 1

Solve Questions 1 through 2 using a paper-and-pencil method to divide. Write any remainders as whole numbers. Check your work using multiplication.

1. $17\overline{)982}$

2. $24\overline{)2694}$

Assessment Blackline Master

Part 2

As you answer questions on this part of the test, you may use any of the tools you have used in class. For example, you may wish to use a calculator, a ruler, and pattern blocks.

3. Mr. Moreno traveled 455 miles in a two-week period. What is the average number of miles he traveled each day?

4. **A.** Mr. Moreno bought and used 42 gallons of fuel for $58.38 during the two-week period. If Mr. Moreno traveled about the same number of miles each day, estimate the average cost of fuel each day.

   B. About how many miles can Mr. Moreno travel on one gallon of fuel?

5. Mr. Moreno and his wife went on a road trip. They decided to switch drivers every 75 miles. If the road trip lasted 889 miles, how many times did they switch drivers?

6. Use exponents to rename each number below as a product of its prime factors. Organize your work in a factor tree.

A. 315   **B.** 440

7. Reduce each fraction to lowest terms.

    A. $\frac{12}{18} =$ _____

    B. $\frac{8}{32} =$ _____

    C. $\frac{9}{24} =$ _____

8. Rename each decimal as a fraction. Reduce the fraction to lowest terms.

    A. $0.8 =$ _____

    B. $0.75 =$ _____

    C. Write this fraction as a decimal: $\frac{15}{24} =$ _____

9. **A.** Using the coordinates given, plot the shape below.

B. Write the ordered pairs in the table.

Ordered Pair	x-coordinate	y-coordinate
	-1	1
	1	1
	3	3
	1	3

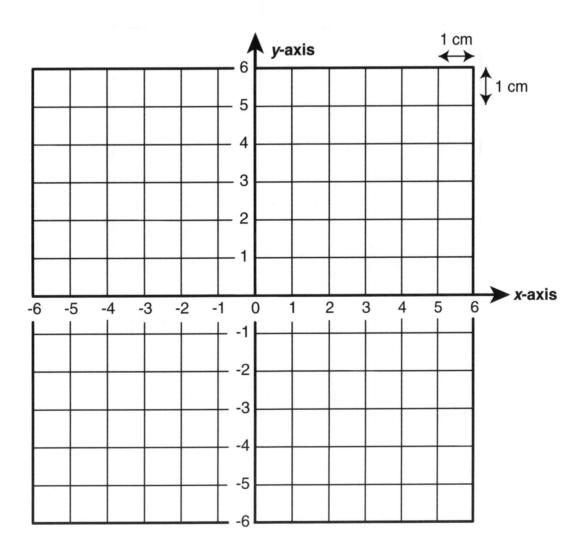

10. Garbage collectors drop off waste at two sites each day. One site collects nonrecyclable waste while the other site collects recyclable waste. The map below shows the two sites.

   A. Write the coordinates for each site on the map.

   B. Use the map to find the actual distance between the sites.

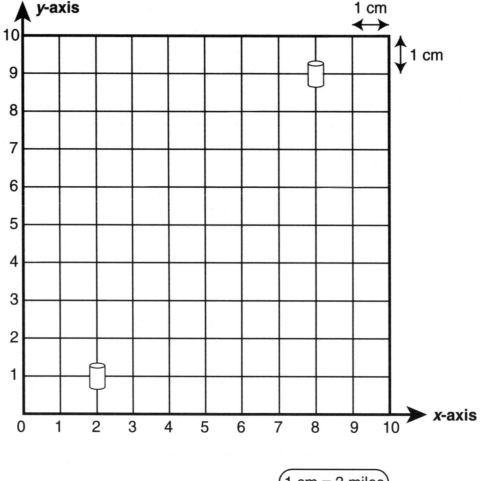

1 cm ≡ 3 miles

11. The Johnny Appleseed Company has decided to sell a special gift box of apples with 18 apples. If $\frac{2}{3}$ of the apples are red, how many of the apples are red? Show how you solved the problem.

12. Solve $\frac{1}{4} \times \frac{2}{3}$ following these steps:
   - Solve the problem and write a number sentence. Be sure your answer is in lowest terms.

   - Record your work on the diagram below.

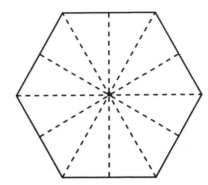

13. To make cookies, David mixed $3\frac{3}{4}$ cups of flour with $1\frac{2}{3}$ cups of sugar in a bowl. How many cups of flour and sugar did David have in the bowl? Show how you solved the problem.

14. Complete the following problems. Give your answer in lowest terms.

   A. $\frac{1}{6} + \frac{2}{9} =$

   B. $\frac{5}{8} - \frac{3}{8} =$

   C. $\frac{1}{15} + \frac{3}{5} =$

Discovery Assignment Book

**Home Practice (DAB p. 192)

Part 7. Food for Thought

Questions 1–5

1. **A.** $\frac{1}{2}$ pizza

   B. $\frac{1}{4}$ pizza

2. $\frac{5}{8}$ of the pie

3. $3\frac{3}{4}$ cups

4. Yes; the punch is $5\frac{1}{4} + 2\frac{2}{3} = 7\frac{11}{12}$ cups. Since 2 quarts is 8 cups and the punch is only $7\frac{11}{12}$ cups, David can pour all the punch into a 2-quart pitcher.

5. 9 pans of muffins

Unit Resource Guide

Midterm Test (URG pp. 72–77)

Questions 1–14

1. 57 R13

2. 112 R6

3. $32\frac{1}{2}$ miles or 32.5 miles

4. **A.** About $4

   B. About 10 or 11 miles

5. 11 times

6. **A.** $315 = 3^2 \times 5 \times 7$. Factor trees will vary. One possible solution is shown.

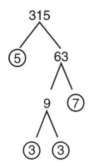

B. $440 = 2^3 \times 5 \times 11$. Factor trees will vary. One possible solution is shown.

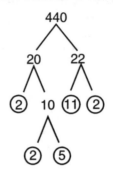

7. **A.** $\frac{2}{3}$ **B.** $\frac{1}{4}$ **C.** $\frac{3}{8}$

8. **A.** $\frac{8}{10} = \frac{4}{5}$ **B.** $\frac{75}{100} = \frac{3}{4}$ **C.** 0.625

9. **A.**

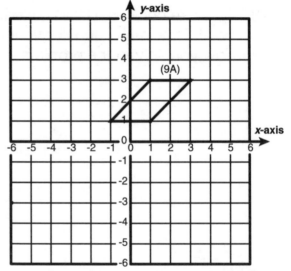

B.

Ordered Pair	x-coordinate	y-coordinate
(-1, 1)	-1	1
(1, 1)	1	1
(3, 3)	3	3
(1, 3)	1	3

10. (2, 1), (8, 9); The sites are 10 cm apart. Using the scale, this is 30 miles.

---

*Answers and/or discussion are included in the Lesson Guide.

**Answers for all the Home Practice in the *Discovery Assignment Book* are at the end of the unit.

11. 12, Solution strategies will vary.

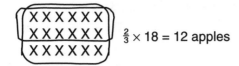
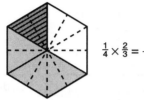 $\frac{2}{3} \times 18 = 12$ apples

12.

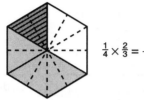 $\frac{1}{4} \times \frac{2}{3} = \frac{1 \times 2}{4 \times 3} = \frac{2}{12} = \frac{1}{6}$

13. $5\frac{5}{12}$

14. **A.** $\frac{7}{18}$ **B.** $\frac{1}{4}$ **C.** $\frac{2}{3}$

*Answers and/or discussion are included in the Lesson Guide.
**Answers for all the Home Practice in the *Discovery Assignment Book* are at the end of the unit.

Discovery Assignment Book

Part 1. Multiplication and Division Practice

Questions 1–2 (DAB p. 189)

1. **A.** $1494\frac{1}{2}$ **B.** $117\frac{1}{2}$

   C. 2214   **D.** 80

   E. 420

2. Answers will vary: Possible response for
   1E: $105 \times 4 = 100 \times 4 + 5 \times 4 =$
   $400 + 20 = 420$

Part 2. Division Practice

Questions 1–2 (DAB p. 189)

1. **A.** $8\frac{1}{4}$ **B.** $8\frac{4}{9}$

   C. $8\frac{1}{2}$ **D.** $10\frac{8}{10} = 10\frac{4}{5}$

   E. $7\frac{5}{7}$ **F.** $6\frac{5}{6}$

   G. $5\frac{2}{8} = 5\frac{1}{4}$ **H.** $3\frac{5}{6}$

   I. $8\frac{3}{8}$

2. **A.** $86\frac{12}{16} = 86\frac{3}{4}$

   B. $769\frac{22}{24} = 769\frac{11}{12}$

   C. $1373\frac{20}{32} = 1373\frac{5}{8}$

Part 3. Fractions

Questions 1–2 (DAB p. 190)

1. **A.** 5   **B.** 3

   C. $\frac{1}{9}$ **D.** $\frac{1}{6}$

   E. $\frac{1}{30}$ **F.** 6

   G. 50¢   **H.** $20

   I. $18

2. Two possible strategies: $\frac{1}{5} \times \frac{5}{6} = \frac{5}{30} = \frac{1}{6}$;
   $\frac{1}{5}$ of 5 is 1, so $\frac{1}{5}$ of $\frac{5}{6}$ is $\frac{1}{6}$.

Part 4. Analyze the Class

Questions 1–5 (DAB p. 190)

1. 6   2. 8

3. $\frac{3}{4}$ 4. 75%

5. $\frac{1}{2}$

Part 5. Let's Practice

Questions A–F (DAB p. 191)

A. $11\frac{1}{20}$ **B.** 7758

C. 3196   **D.** 54.112

E. 815 R6 or $815\frac{2}{3}$ **F.** 67.35

Part 6. Working with Coordinates

Question 1 (DAB p. 191)

1. **A.**

Point	x-coordinate	y-coordinate	Ordered Pair
A	-2	-1	(-2, -1)
B	-3	-3	(-3, -3)
C	-1	-3	(-1, -3)
D	1	3	(1, 3)

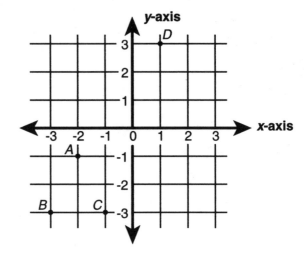

B. 1000 cm

Part 7. Food for Thought

Questions 1–5 (DAB p. 192)

1. **A.** $\frac{1}{2}$ pizza
   B. $\frac{1}{4}$ pizza

2. $\frac{5}{8}$ of the pie

3. $3\frac{3}{4}$ cups

4. Yes; the punch is $5\frac{1}{4} + 2\frac{2}{3} = 7\frac{11}{12}$ cups. Since
   2 quarts is 8 cups and the punch is only
   $7\frac{11}{12}$ cups, David can pour all the punch into a
   2-quart pitcher.

5. 9 pans of muffins

*Answers and/or discussion are included in the Lesson Guide.